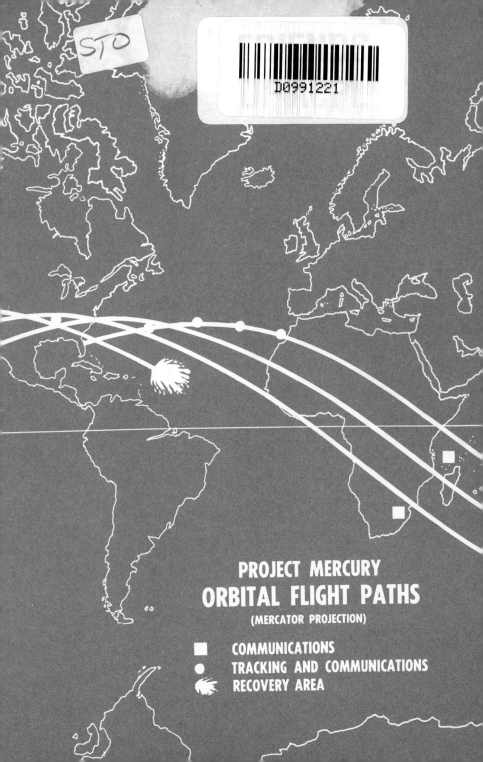

PROJECT MERCURY
ORBITAL FLIGHT PATHS
(MERCATOR PROJECTION)

- ■ COMMUNICATIONS
- ● TRACKING AND COMMUNICATIONS
- RECOVERY AREA

SEVEN INTO SPACE

SEVEN INTO SPACE

THE STORY OF THE MERCURY ASTRONAUTS

by Joseph N. Bell

Popular Mechanics Company
200 East Ontario Street
Chicago, Illinois

Jacket design by Robert Borja
Illustrations by David Hewitt

PHOTO CREDITS:

Associated Press pp. 14, 15, 96, 121, 125; Joseph
Fletcher pp. 67, 70, 75, 77, 79, 81, 86, 88, 93,
100, 114; Mrs. Robert Goddard pp. 25, 26; Mount
Wilson and Palomar Observatories pp. 16, 170;
and Sovfoto pp. 41, 42, 45, 47.

Other photographs through the courtesy of:
Boeing Airplane Co.; Convair Div., General Dy-
namics Corp.; Lockheed Aircraft Corp.; National
Aeronautics and Space Administration; Radio
Corporation of America; Rocketdyne Div., North
American Aviation; U.S. Air Force; U.S. Army;
and U.S. Navy.

*To Janet,
whose patience, understanding, encouragement,
and magical management made all this possible.*

ACKNOWLEDGMENTS

In a period when much is being written about outer space, it would be both difficult and deadly to list all the written sources consulted in the preparation of this book. To the writers, scientists, and technicians who authored the hundreds of papers and articles which I read on various aspects of space and space flight, my appreciation and thanks.

Although many people helped me considerably in producing this book, I feel a very special gratitude to the editors of *Popular Mechanics* magazine — particularly Cliff Hicks, Rod Grant, and the late Wayne Whittaker — who not only continued to believe in this project, but gave me freely the support and encouragement I needed through the many months of research effort.

Thanks, also, to Joe Fletcher, *PM* photographer whose pictures add so much to these pages, to the Astronauts' intrepid front man, Col. John "Shorty" Powers, who never failed to provide help when I needed it, and to the Astronauts themselves, who were unflinchingly patient and unfailingly cooperative.

Gratitude is also due the Russians, who thoughtfully failed to orbit a manned satellite while this book was in preparation.

June 1, 1960   *Joseph N. Bell*

CONTENTS

CHAPTER ONE

COUNTDOWN!

"The immensity of the universe becomes a matter of satisfaction rather than awe; we are citizens of no mean city."
—*Sir James Jeans, British physicist*

"Zero minus 75," says the bland, impersonal voice in his headphones. He's strapped in the same contour couch that supported his underside so many times during training flights on the centrifuge at Johnsville. But now its feel is different. The friendliness of a well-worn garment has disappeared in the crisp pre-dawn at Cape Canaveral. The couch feels cold and damp, and the restraining straps unfriendly.

He shrugs aside these feelings because he's had them many times before and knows how to cope with them. He can't swallow the fear entirely, though. There's still a lump of it congesting his stomach — but he long ago learned to live with that, too.

His name is John or Gus or Scott or Al or Deke or Gordon or Wally. And he's about to be blasted into the greatest adventure ever embarked on by man. He's scared and awed because he's an intelligent — a highly intelligent — human being, and the significance of this moment in history can't be completely immersed in the mechanical requirements of the last minutes before firing. He senses the momentousness, but he can't wallow in it. There are too many other things to be done, things on which his life — and, almost as important to him, the success of Project Mercury — depend.

"Zero minus 70," drones the headset.

He recalls wondering — in the few introspective moments he allowed himself during the two years of training for this flight into space — if he would review his life in the seconds before blast-off. Would he think about home and family? About the hours in combat when he had faced death so often without time, really, to grapple with the idea until the immediate moment of hazard was over? About the hours of test flying when, with a new and unproven aircraft — like the one he was in now — he had exulted in proving his dominion over it, making it do what he wanted it to do?

He's surprised to realize he'd been thinking of none of these things. There had been no quiet in which to think, no end to the ceaseless checking and re-checking of instruments, of reviewing emergency procedures, of questions and answers, of that sexless, bodiless, emotionless voice saying . . .

"Zero minus 60."

A light flashes on the instrument panel before him. One minute to go. It's been 54 minutes since he climbed awkwardly up the 75 feet of the Atlas gantry, looking down finally on an ant hill of activity below him, hundreds of men and machines scurrying about in the semi-darkness on carefully rehearsed missions, all aimed at producing the one convulsive effort that would launch him, finally, into space.

He'd crawled carefully into the capsule, squeezing under the maze of wires and instruments, ever respectful of them for he knew what a single crossed wire or fouled instrument might cost. Solicitous hands had strapped him in the couch. Four of the other Astronauts had been there on the gantry with him. There wasn't room for handshakes, but such ceremony was unnecessary. Their eyes had said it. "Good luck. I wish it were me instead of you." And strangely enough — although the world could never understand — they meant it.

Then the capsule door had closed, he latched it from inside, and he was alone. That had been his only rough moment so far — that first instant of solitude before the questions and instructions in his headset shattered the forbidding loneliness of the knowledge that below and about him, the gantry was being moved away, and the firing area was methodically being cleared of men and vehicles. He'd had one fleeting thought of a gallows with the crowd being pushed back before the trap was sprung — but he'd been able to laugh at the idea and even voice it jokingly on his radio.

The Astronaut on the other end had said, "No noose is good noose," and the constriction that was building inside him loosened and relaxed.

It was good to have four of the Astronauts to talk with at the blockhouse. They could understand what was going on in the capsule — and in his thoughts — without needless explanation. Soon he'd hear the other two — one at the tracking station in Australia, the other with the rescue fleet that would salvage him from the Atlantic in about three and one-half hours. All seven had been prepared to go. There had been no show of nerves or emotion when the decision had been announced to the group a week ago. Only a handclasp and a wisecrack from each of them — as he knew it would be.

Thank God there had been no overpowering emotion at home, either. It was a moment for which they had all long been prepared. Neither his wife nor any of the children had said, "Why did it have to be you?" That would have made things difficult for him, and they knew it, and they didn't say it.

Now he hears, "Zero minus 30," and his eyes caress the instrument panel and flick over the periscope screen slightly behind and above it. He can see only blackness now, but in a few minutes there will be sights visible to him that have never before been seen by earthmen. The firmament with its fences down. The earth with its horizons lifted. For the first time, excitement grows inside him. The procedures have all been reviewed. Or almost all . . .

"Check the location of your abort switch once more," a new voice in the headset is saying. "If an emergency abort is necessary, you'll be ejected automatically — otherwise, we'll talk it over. Okay?"

He replies "Roger" automatically, and the countdown picks up again at "Zero minus 15."

His excitement is chilled for an instant by the word, *abort*. As he climbed into the capsule, he could see overhead, silhouetted against the clear night sky, the emergency system. If all went well, it would fall away when it was no longer needed. But if the Atlas beneath him — the complex, multi-million-dollar maze of electronic ingeniousness — tilted off course, or if any one of a thousand things that could go wrong did go wrong, then a push and twist of the abort handle would send him rocketing away from the Atlas, 2,500 feet into the air, to be let down by parachute into the ocean in what would be an unparalleled piece of anti-climacticism.

"There are 10 seconds to zero."

He raises his hand ponderously off the arm rest, and his gloved fingers touch the control handle. He won't need this for awhile. But when he does . . . His stomach muscles tighten and his body tingles. The space suit that envelops him — the same suit he had crawled in and out of so many times at Langley Field — feels suddenly oppressive. He squirms inside it and comes up against the restraining straps that will prevent him from floating off the couch when the capsule orbits and he becomes weightless.

"Zero minus seven."

He remembers the first time he was catapulted off an aircraft carrier deck, and he tells himself that's what this will be like. The ear-splitting noise, the almost intolerable seconds of pressure, of being pushed down and down into the cockpit, then the exhilaration of free flight. Just like that, he tells himself, only now he'll be more comfortable because he's reclining instead of sitting up. The charge is a little stronger, he reflects wryly, but the idea is the same.

"Zero minus five."

"God bless you," he hears unexpectedly on the headset, and he knows the Astronaut saying the words speaks for the dedicated people tensely sweating out this moment at Cape Canaveral — and millions of others who will learn about it over their breakfast coffee later this morning . . .

"We interrupt this program to announce that the United States has successfully put a man in orbit . . ."

"Zero minus three."

He realizes a little reproachfully that he hadn't spent any of the last hour thinking about God. He does so now. His lips move inside the face window of his space suit.

"Zero minus two . . ."

"Zero minus one."

Eternity stands suspended.

Here's how the earth will look to an orbiting Mercury Astronaut. This photograph, taken from an Atlas missile, shows the West Indies with South America on the horizon.

Then all the thunderclaps in history reunite for a brief instant beneath him.

The weight of a hundred mountains slowly begins to engulf him and push him down and down into the couch until it seems he must come out the other side.

His body strains.

His eyes bulge.

But his thoughts remain clear and concise, focused on the instrument panel, searching for warnings of trouble.

Then he hears a shout of sheer delight and exuberance in his headset, and he knows the launching has been successful.

The exhilaration of taking this new spacecraft aloft, of breaking bonds with earthbound humans rolls over him in great, shattering waves, and he knows an excitement so intense that it seems he can no longer contain it.

Two continents are visible in this photograph, also taken from an Atlas missile in flight. Africa is at lower left and South America is on the horizon at center.

The first American has been launched into space.

Dawn breaks bright and clear over Cape Canaveral — the dawn of a new day and a new era. Staring into the rising sun at the disappearing speck that a few moments before had towered over Cape Canaveral are some of the thousands of men and women who worked for many years that this day and this event might take place.

This is their story — and the story of the seven men who stand at the pinnacle of their efforts: the Mercury Astronauts.

CHAPTER TWO

BEFORE
THE ASTRONAUTS

"Science and technology have reached the stage
where the next logical step is outward. As Mark
Twain quoted an old Mississippi River pilot on
a great technical advance of another day: 'When
it's steamboat time, you steamboat.' . . . Now,
it is space time."
        —*T. Keith Glennan, NASA administrator*

There is little in the daily experience of the average
American to condition him to think in terms of the universality of space. Each year, the American citizen becomes
more dependent on clearly defined boundaries within which
he can live comfortably. He wants to know exactly what
to expect. A life span of so many years. A speed limit of
so many miles per hour. A salary bracket of so much
money. A summer and winter of so many days.

The universe doesn't fit this pattern. It breaks down all
existing boundaries of thought. As a result, it is ignored by
most Americans, misunderstood by many of those who take
the time to consider it, and accepted and understood by
only a handful of pioneers who are willing to start from a
mental jumping-off place beyond which most human beings
refuse to venture.

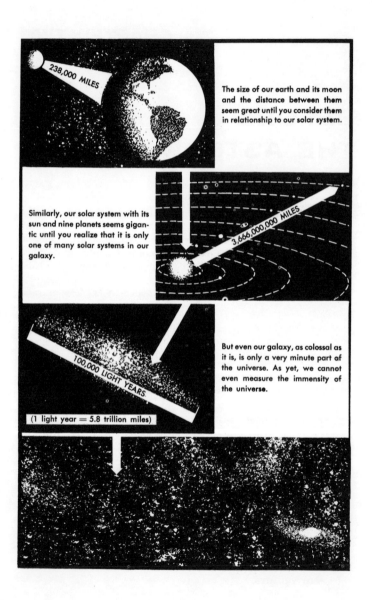

238,000 MILES

The size of our earth and its moon and the distance between them seem great until you consider them in relationship to our solar system.

Similarly, our solar system with its sun and nine planets seems gigantic until you realize that it is only one of many solar systems in our galaxy.

3,666,000,000 MILES

100,000 LIGHT YEARS

(1 light year = 5.8 trillion miles)

But even our galaxy, as colossal as it is, is only a very minute part of the universe. As yet, we cannot even measure the immensity of the universe.

Consider, for a moment, some of the incredible statistics of space:

We inhabit a tiny planet revolving about a minor star which is only one star in a galaxy of some *200 billion* stars. If we had started to count the stars in our galaxy at the rate of 100 stars a minute at the time Christ was born, we would just now be finishing the count.

Traveling at 10,000 m.p.h., it would take us a day to reach the moon, a year to reach the sun, and 40 years to arrive at Pluto — the farthest planet of our solar system. It would take 270,000 years to approach the nearest star (Alpha Centauri), and we would still be a long way from leaving our galaxy.

And our galaxy is only a pinprick in the heavens. There are billions of other galaxies within 2 billion light-years of earth, the present limit of our largest telescope, and there is every reason to suppose that there are countless more beyond that distance.

These are not facts to be considered prosaically, like next week's grocery list or the payment on the TV set. They are stupendous, marvelous facts that require a new dimension of thinking, a mental gear-shifting that *must* accompany the Space Age. And for a few, of course, this sort of thinking has preceded the Space Age. This is the stuff of which pioneers are made.

Nor do these facts diminish the stature of man. It's too easy to dismiss man as an insignificant cipher in the formulae of space and go back to the television set. But quite the opposite is true. Man takes on a new and greater significance in the light of space thinking, for only through the mind of man can the universality of space be comprehended — and its frontiers penetrated. The men who have accepted this elevated stature and risen to this challenge are the men who are today probing space for answers to age-old questions. Mankind has always been curious about space. In 1960, a small band of adventurers will satisfy some of that curiosity by first-hand observation.

Why this consuming curiosity? Space is one of the great unknowns that remains to be explored. The dictionary tells us that space is the "interval between objects." What interval? And what objects? The space pioneers intend to find out. And soon. And nothing is going to stop them.

Already they've assembled much basic information. For example, they know that:

Space is a perfect vacuum, offering no restriction to vehicle movement;

Earth's gravitational pull is slight enough and its atmosphere thin enough that relatively low velocities will permit escape;

Objects orbiting in space are weightless because the centrifugal effects of whizzing around the earth are exactly balanced by the force of gravity;

Intense heat and radiation exist in space, but not in sufficient quantity or intensity to prevent interplanetary travel if proper precautions are taken.

When scientists talk about space, they are usually referring to the area above 60 miles altitude; below this lies all but one-millionth of the earth's atmosphere. They are also likely to consider space in two zones. The near-space now being explored with rockets and satellites (which includes everything within the orbit of earth's moon) is called cislunar space. Beyond lies translunar space — limitless and beckoning.

* * *

Since the beginnings of recorded history, men have been chasing stars. Never before have we been so close to catching up with one.

It was in the 13th century that the Chinese discovered

British Col. William Congreve made one of the first basic modifications of the rocket when he put a "tail" on it to stabilize and direct its flight.

"By the rocket's red glare" . . . **This is how Baltimore harbor looked to Francis Scott Key as British men-o'-war threw up a barrage of rockets at the American defenders.**

space could best be pursued by means of the rocket. The rocket is based on a principle that wasn't articulated until Sir Isaac Newton's law, hundreds of years after the first Chinese rockets were built and fired. Stated simply, it is: "For every action there is an equal and opposite reaction."

If you dive off the rear of a rowboat, you can observe this principle. Your dive pushes the boat forward with a force equal to your weight times the speed of your dive. Similarly, if you throw rocks away from the rear of the boat, it will be pushed ahead. Rocketry makes use of the same simple principle. Burning gases in the rocket escape through the rear, thrusting the rocket forward or up. As the atmosphere becomes thinner, the thrust of the gases is correspondingly greater and the rocket moves faster.

Perhaps the earliest astronaut was a Chinese scientist named Wan Hu. He had himself strapped in a couch not too dissimilar to those being used by the Astronauts of to-day. Wan Hu's couch, however, had no protective vehicle around it. It was just a couch, to which several dozen crude — but lethal — rockets were attached. The rockets were fired simultaneously — and the couch and Wan Hu disappeared in a tremendous explosion. If Wan Hu attained the heavens he sought, it was by an even more direct route than rocketry.

After Wan Hu's experiment, the pursuit of rocketry advanced slowly. Its next impetus came from the Chinese warlords' use of "flaming fire arrows." These early rockets were used to beat back the Mongols when they besieged Peking. Several hundred years later, rockets turned up again when Hindu troops fighting the British fired thousands of rockets powered by black powder. This introduced rocketry to the Western World, and it was quickly picked up by British Col. William Congreve. He positioned sticks on rockets to stabilize their flight; by this means, he achieved ranges of 2,000 yards — then considered a tremendous accomplishment.

In the early 1800's, the use of rockets in warfare became quite common. The British used rockets to bombard Cologne, destroy Copenhagen, and help defeat Napoleon. In 1812, a young American poet named Francis Scott Key peered through the bars of a prison ship and watched the attack on Baltimore's Fort McHenry by "the rocket's red glare." This wasn't poetic license; Key was describing real rockets.

The U. S. Army fired its first rocket in 1846; soon after, an American named William Hale introduced canted fins to provide the stability and accuracy long lacking in rocketry. But rifled cannons proved still more accurate and more deadly, so rockets once again were consigned to limbo until World War I, when the French, Russians, and Germans used them from aircraft against both air (mainly balloons) and ground targets. The German, Prof. Hugo Junkers, also used powder rockets during World War I to assist heavily-loaded aircraft to become airborne.

Shortly before the first World War, a young physics instructor at the Worcester (Mass.) Polytechnic Institute named Robert H. Goddard was frightening his neighbors with his do-it-yourself rockets which he manufactured and tested at home. Since the spectacular demise of Wan Hu some 700 years earlier, men had been using rockets primarily as destructive weapons. But, like his earlier Chinese counterpart, Robert Goddard saw in the rocket a means for exploring the heavens. Unhappily his vision was not appreciated; Goddard was years ahead of his time.

He was fascinated by Newton's First Law of Motion which says that "every body persists in a state of rest or of uniform motion in a straight line unless compelled by external force to change its state." To Robert Goddard, this meant that once a rocket could be fired clear of the earth's restraining atmosphere, it would continue in motion without any additional propellant force until some counter force slowed it down. Here was the key to possible interplanetary travel. But Newton's law completely refuted the long-held belief — first put forward by Aristotle — that an external force must be constantly applied to keep a body in motion.

"Not so," said Newton, and Robert Goddard said, "Amen."

No one encouraged Goddard in his rocket experiments, and the clamor of his neighbors drove him from Massachusetts to the deserts of New Mexico to continue his work. Within a 15-year span, Dr. Goddard:

Successfully launched the first liquid-fueled rocket;
Produced the first gyro-stabilized rocket;

Dr. Robert Goddard was the "father of American rocketry," a scientific genius whose work—now being given the recognition due it—was largely ignored by Americans during his lifetime.

25

Here is one of the later (1940) Goddard experiments, a pump-driven rocket. The launching site is near Roswell, N. Mex., where Goddard was forced to go to carry out his experiments.

26

Consistently fired rockets much faster (700 m.p.h.) and much higher (7,500 feet) than had ever been done before;

Invented the recoilless rocket launcher which, ignored by the American military in 1918, became the famed bazooka of World War II.

During the next two decades Dr. Goddard tried in vain to interest other Americans in his experiments. But they hadn't the time or inclination to listen. The rigor mortis of isolationism had set in. Americans cared little about their earthly neighbors, and nothing at all about their interstellar neighbors. But across the sea, Goddard's work was studied carefully by members of the German Society for Space Travel. A few years later the members of this society developed the German V-2 rocket, which for a time threatened almost single-handedly to save the day for Germany in World War II.

Other nations were listening, too. Dr. Goddard set forth the principles of the multi-stage rocket which the Russians used to put Sputnik I into orbit in 1957. Thirty years earlier he had theorized that a rocket could be sent to an altitude of 580 miles — roughly the point at which Sputnik went into orbit.

Robert Goddard was the father of modern-day rocketry. America had within its grasp — in the work of Dr. Goddard — the necessary knowledge to leave the rest of the world far behind in the development of rockets and guided missiles. Had we listened to him, the world situation might be quite different today.

But we didn't listen, and thus had to muddle through on the coat-tails of the V-2. After World War II, both Russia and the United States acquired a quantity of German rockets and German scientists and went to work. And the race — the most lethal race in the history of mankind — was on.

This rocket almost turned the tide for Germany in World War II. Captured in possession of a German prisoner, this photograph shows a V-2 ready for launching against an Allied air base.

BEFORE THE ASTRONAUTS

The United States got off to a fast start. America's first Wac Corporal rocket was fired to a height of 43 miles in 1945. Another truly significant advance in American rocket development came in 1949 with the "Bumper Project", in which a Wac Corporal was successfully launched as an upper-stage vehicle of a V-2.

This was an exciting — almost breathtaking — experiment that proved the feasibility of staging rocket vehicles at high altitudes. For the second time, the United States had scored a dramatic first in space, but the American public still wasn't interested. Indeed, it was downright bored. Space experiments were generally looked upon as expensive nonsense of no real significance.

So, once again, the United States faltered when it had a chance to pull away in the space race. After the Bumper experiment, little was accomplished. Speaking of this period some years later, Dr. Wernher von Braun — the former German scientist who has now become America's chief missile expert — said:

"Right after the war, public interest in the United States turned away from weapons toward consumer goods. Few people in this country realized that the rulers of the Soviet Union were in no mood to lose their wartime gains through hasty disarmament. There was no ballistic missile development program in the United States between 1945 and 1951 because there was no obvious need for it, no interest for it, no money for it."

During this period missile development was scattered among three dozen different programs and supervised by Federal agencies that often had no contact with one another. In addition to the armed services, which loudly and jealously insisted on exclusive rights to develop their own missile programs, probably the most important agency involved in missile development was the National Advisory

Committee for Aeronautics (NACA). Its principal claim to pre-eminence was seniority; it had been around for some 40 years, primarily for the purpose of directing research programs aimed at solving problems of flight. Until the end of World War II, these problems were concerned almost entirely with airplanes.

In order to keep pace with overseas competition after the war, it was vital that NACA's work be concentrated on rockets. But this wasn't quite so easy to bring off in America as in Russia, where single-mindedness of purpose under absolute state control could and did prevail.

Here, again, is Dr. Von Braun, describing what happened in the United States: "We turned research and development projects on and off like a faucet, depending on the shifting situation with regard to budget and priority. And every time we turned one research and development project or contract off, several years of priceless experience on the part of a few individuals went down the drain. We needed to learn to grow and preserve teams. We do it in baseball. Why not in research and development, too?"

Why not, indeed?

There were many reasons why the United States of the early 50's wasn't ready to invest in the long term, dedicated (and expensive) research work necessary to bring us forth as a leader in the space race. Some are excusable in the self-righteous rationale of hindsight; some aren't.

We were struggling to balance the federal budget; outer space seemed a frivolous place for deficit spending;

We were struggling to preserve the balance of power in conventional armaments; it was difficult to fit space hardware into this picture;

We were absorbed with our own material self-sufficiency; automatic dishwashers and color television seemed much more important than exploring the universe;

BEFORE THE ASTRONAUTS

We were apathetic to the threat from Russia; it was inconceivable to Americans that any backward Asiatic nation could challenge their supremacy in such a field as science and technology;

We were mentally lazy, lacking the vision and courage to put money and effort into the sort of basic research that might have carried us into space first;

We lacked imagination — the chief ingredient of enlightened research. In this area, where we should most roundly have licked the Soviets, we failed most abysmally.

Small wonder the emotional shock waves that bounded and rebounded through the United States as Americans perceived the world-wide admiration won by Russia when the Soviets put the first artificial satellite into orbit on October 4, 1957.

At first, when we should have hitched up our belt, spat on our hands, and gotten down to work, we blithely deprecated the Russian feat, down-played the importance of space, and made excuses for our lagging efforts. But all this mouthing rang hollow to a world greatly impressed by Sputnik I. When we finally turned to the business of catching up with the Russians in space, we were several years — at least — behind the Soviets. This was the formidable job laid in the lap of the National Aeronautics and Space Administration (NASA) when it was formed by Act of Congress in 1958.

* * *

The National Aeronautics and Space Administration began operating officially on Wednesday, October 1, 1958. It took over the functions of the 43-year-old National Advisory Committee for Aeronautics, and assumed control of NACA's staff of 7,960 scientists, engineers, technicians, and administrative employees, its Washington, D.C. headquarters, and five laboratories and field stations.

SPACE CHAIN OF COMMAND

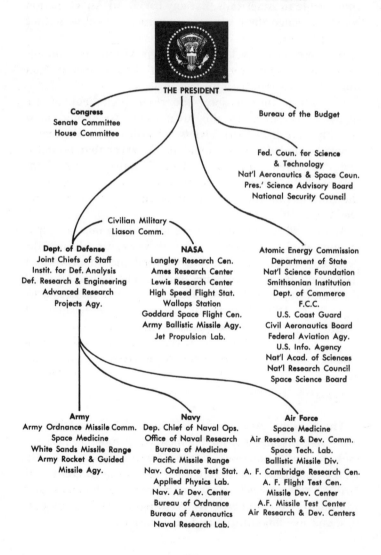

THE PRESIDENT

Congress
Senate Committee
House Committee

Bureau of the Budget

Fed. Coun. for Science
& Technology
Nat'l Aeronautics & Space Coun.
Pres.' Science Advisory Board
National Security Council

Civilian Military
Liason Comm.

Dept. of Defense
Joint Chiefs of Staff
Instit. for Def. Analysis
Def. Research & Engineering
Advanced Research
Projects Agy.

NASA
Langley Research Cen.
Ames Research Center
Lewis Research Center
High Speed Flight Stat.
Wallops Station
Goddard Space Flight Cen.
Army Ballistic Missile Agy.
Jet Propulsion Lab.

Atomic Energy Commission
Department of State
Nat'l Science Foundation
Smithsonian Institution
Dept. of Commerce
F.C.C.
U.S. Coast Guard
Civil Aeronautics Board
Federal Aviation Agy.
U.S. Info. Agency
Nat'l Acad. of Sciences
Nat'l Research Council
Space Science Board

Army
Army Ordnance Missile Comm.
Space Medicine
White Sands Missile Range
Army Rocket & Guided
Missile Agy.

Navy
Dep. Chief of Naval Ops.
Office of Naval Research
Bureau of Medicine
Pacific Missile Range
Nav. Ordnance Test Stat.
Applied Physics Lab.
Nav. Air Dev. Center
Bureau of Ordnance
Bureau of Aeronautics
Naval Research Lab.

Air Force
Space Medicine
Air Research & Dev. Comm.
Space Tech. Lab.
Ballistic Missile Div.
A. F. Cambridge Research Cen.
A. F. Flight Test Cen.
Missile Dev. Center
A.F. Missile Test Center
Air Research & Dev. Centers

President Eisenhower also transferred to NASA some of the assorted do-it-yourself missile projects going on in other parts of the government. The Navy Vanguard program, several Air Force space projects, and the Army Jet Propulsion Laboratory in Los Angeles were stowed early under the NASA wing. For the first time, the United States was making a pass at a coordinated attack on space problems.

The National Aeronautics and Space Act of 1958 which established NASA emphasized two primary points:

"It is the policy of the United States that activities in space should be directed to peaceful purpose for the benefit of all mankind;

"The general welfare and security of the United States *require* that adequate provision be made for aeronautical and space activities."

There were those citizens in 1958 — and there are still a considerable number of them — who look on ventures in space as comic-book frivolity for soft-headed children. They ask, "Why should we expend increasing amounts of time, money, and effort to stake our claim in outer space when millions of people are starving right here on earth?"

These people deserve an answer — and some sound ones are readily available. There are four basic and compelling reasons why the United States should not be left behind in space:

(1) The opportunities for scientific advancement in many fields of great practical benefit;

(2) The need to assure that full advantage is taken of the military potential of space;

(3) The competition with Russia for national prestige among other nations of the world;

(4) The irresistible urge of man to explore the unknown.

Let's examine each of these reasons briefly. Satellites open new avenues for research in all the earth sciences. The plotting of satellite trajectories will finally enable us to determine the exact configuration of the earth — an extremely important element in the origin, history, and structure of our planet. Data received from the cosmic ray laboratory above the earth's atmosphere can provide us with an incomparably greater knowledge of the universe than we now have.

An eminent Russian scientist said recently: "Astronomers have always been enormously handicapped because our observatories and scientific stations are at the bottom of the air ocean which envelops the earth, an ocean hundreds of miles deep. We have dreamed of observatories outside the atmosphere, and the satellites have brought our dreams closer to reality."

But these are generalities. What specific practical benefits can reasonably be expected from these new vistas in space opened to science?

Man-made satellites for the first time will give weathermen a direct look at the movements of great air masses and storm fronts. Accurate long-range weather predictions will then be possible, giving advanced warning to areas threatened by violent weather. Such predictions would also be advantageous in warfare and industry. As Dr. Fred Singer, Maryland University physics professor, pointed out recently: "There isn't an industry in the country that isn't affected in some way by the weather. Right now, we get only partial weather surveillance with only 5 percent of the earth under observation — and most of that in the United States."

The use of satellites for reference points makes possible a much more accurate measurement of distances. For example, the location of some Pacific island groups such as

BEFORE THE ASTRONAUTS

One of the "firsts" scored by the U.S. in the space race was this Tiros weather satellite. It was orbited to provide weather data, principally by means of televised pictures.

The workings of the Tiros weather satellite are the most complex of any electronic system we have sent into space. The 42-inch-diameter satellite has two television cameras.

the Marshalls may differ as much as four miles by present chartings. These errors will be corrected — and air and sea navigators will benefit.

Communication possibilities through the use of satellites are almost limitless. World-wide television and radio transmission could be accomplished easily and effectively by bouncing signals off satellites — thus bringing the peoples of the world even closer to each other than they are now.

These same benefits apply to the military, where many important advantages have been obscured by claimed benefits that don't stand up under close examination. One of these is the theory that a nation controlling space could direct bombs to pinpointed targets on the earth below. The fallacy here is that the bombs would also be in orbit and would simply follow the satellite from which they were dropped unless they were equipped with an expensive and complex system of retro-rockets. And such systems aren't necessary, for the same job can be performed much more simply and with deadly accuracy by earth-based intercontinental ballistic missiles.

The principal military objective of space research is defensive. Manned space stations could provide an almost 100-percent efficient warning system against missile attacks. According to Brig. Gen. H. A. Boushey, Air Force deputy director of research and development: "Enemy missiles as they rose above the atmosphere during launching could be detected clearly and warning transmitted in half the time of our best earth-based early warning systems." To a nation that has no intention of ever starting a nuclear war, such defensive benefits are immeasurable.

But over and above the known military advantages of space exploration is the urgent necessity of refusing to permit the Soviet Union to investigate this vast unkown for military advantage without competition from us. There may be profound military advantages in space still to be discovered; the United States simply can't sit on its scientific hands while its chief competitor goes briskly about the business of discovery as the rest of the world looks admiringly on.

Already the United States has lost considerable caste with other nations as a result of the Soviet supremacy in space. The heavens comprise the world's most immense stage. There the contest between the world's two greatest powers is staged before an audience of billions. Admission is free, and all nations are watching and weighing this drama in the sky. Those who underestimate its importance to U. S. prestige are performing a great disservice to the free world. We should be playing with our first team — trained and equipped to the very best of our ability. To do less is to lose touch with destiny.

And finally, regardless of scientific, military, or competitive considerations, man is compelled to explore the unknown. To restrain this urge would be to reduce the stature of man and negate the achievements of the visionary pioneers of the past. The arguments that we should clean up the mess on earth before we begin to poke around in space have no bearing here. Man's exploration of space doesn't, per se, indicate contempt or ignorance or lack of feeling for the acute distress still suffered by a majority of the people on our earth. There's really no connection at all, and to try to force one on our space pioneers indicates a complete misunderstanding of the nature and motives of man. When man is ever told "thus far and no farther," he will cease to become man. Through the lesson of universality to be found in space, the status of man on earth will be enhanced as never before.

These were the primary reasons behind the formation of the National Aeronautics and Space Administration in

1958. At its head is T. Keith Glennan, an ebullient and effective administrator who was given a leave of absence from his job as president of Case Institute of Technology in Cleveland. Glennan had just returned from a trip through Russia with a group of university presidents when his appointment was announced. He recalls: "The Russians are totally engaged in a drive to employ the educational process to win world leadership in technology, and thus to win world leadership in all other matters. Theirs is the fervor of the Crusades. With this fresh in my mind, we were hardly back in Washington when I was asked to head up NASA. For me, it was a case of put up or shut up!" Glennan put up. Since then, he has been the supersalesman of the space business, traveling indefatigably about the country, making hundreds of speeches in an effort to drum up support and enthusiasm for our space program. So far, because of public apathy, he's been only moderately successful.

In the meantime, NASA has grown modestly, mainly by taking over control of assorted space programs that were tucked away in bureaucratic corners. The most sizeable NASA acquisition — and by far the most important — was the transfer, early in 1960, of Wernher von Braun's Development Operations Division of the Army Ballistic Missile Agency. The reason for this transfer, said Administrator Glennan, was "to put under one management the great majority of the government's scientists and engineers who are interested and active in understanding and using the space environment for peaceful purposes."

There is still, however, considerable confusion fostered by the efforts of the Eisenhower Administration to effect a clear delineation between two entities that many say simply can't logically be separated — the civilian and military space programs.

Under the terms of the act which created **NASA**, this agency is responsible for all of the nation's space activities except those "peculiar to or primarily associated with the development of weapons systems, military operation, or the defense of the United States." These activities remain the responsibility of the Department of Defense, and have been delegated to the Air Force. The wasteful and ridiculous competition between services has thus been substantially reduced, although the situation is still far from cleared up and such anomalies as the Air Force competing with itself by producing almost identical missiles, the Atlas and the Titan, still persist. However, our military missile program has slogged ahead, almost in spite of itself, to the point where, given a few more years of grace, we will have a considerable enough deterrent missile force — housed in protected launching sites — to insure complete annihilation of an enemy if we are ever attacked. We can only pray that we be given this time — and that our leaders are far-sighted enough to take maximum advantage of it.

It is not the intent of this book to examine the military missile program beyond the few paragraphs already devoted to it. Once the potential of complete destruction is attained by both the Communist and free world (and we must scramble to make this the case as quickly as possible) further competition at the military level is meaningless. If a war of annihilation is started by either side, civilization on earth will simply be wiped out.

In view of this stalemate, the most likely arena of competition is in space exploration where — unlike our capacity for destruction — we have barely scratched the surface.

As the administrator of our civilian space program, NASA is threshing about valiantly against public apathy, lack of funds, and a shortage of aggressiveness in its own top echelons, to establish the United States as a leader in space.

In 1959, we spent $500 million on this work — about the same amount used for the storage of excess grain. Many Americans have slotted the space program in roughly the same category as farm surpluses. No doubt there will be larger budgets in the years ahead, but we need more than larger budgets for our space program. We need larger thinking.

With the funds supplied it, NASA is carrying on a four-pronged program:

(1) Scientific exploration of the upper atmosphere and outer space, with particular emphasis on meteorology and communications;

(2) A national space-vehicle program for the development of rockets with increased reliability and larger payload capabilities;

(3) Basic space research and technological development;

(4) Manned flight into space, of which Project Mercury is the first step.

Although these programs are interdependent — and all are closely tied in with military missile development — the remainder of this book will be devoted primarily to the story of Project Mercury, the efforts of the United States to put a human being into orbit around the earth.

* * *

When the Russians put a dog named Laika into space in 1958, a popular story on Moscow radio and television went something like this: "The space dog is now flying over Washington. American Senators are worried about whether it will bite." Laika is one dog whose beep turned out to be as bad as its bite; the wounds it inflicted on American prestige have yet to heal.

Since all of America's efforts in space must be assessed against a backdrop of Soviet accomplishment, we should take a look — before considering our own man-into-space

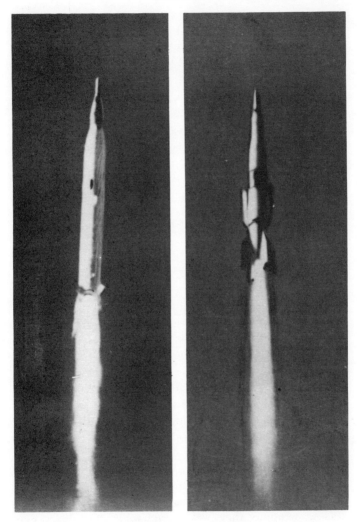

Here are two Russian rockets. Both were launched in connection with the International Geophysical Year. Equipment containers are visible on the side of the rocket at right.

The noted space traveler, Laika, waits calmly—and unsuspectingly— to be sealed into his cabin and carried heavenward in Russia's 1,120- pound satellite, Sputnik II.

program — at what our competition is doing. Where is Russia in her space efforts? How did she get there? And where is she going?

Specific information on the Russian space program isn't available to us. The Soviets tell us what they want us to know and nothing more. A totalitarian state is able to report its successes and bury its failures, and we must presume that is what the Russians have done. Even so, their successes have been considerable.

The Russians began their development of large rockets shortly after World War II. With their customary singleness of purpose, they made an early decision to concentrate on rocket-propelled ICBMs as the delivery system for the nuclear weapons they were developing (while we were relying entirely on the bombers of the Strategic Air Command).

Our initial lack of need for high-thrust ballistic missiles to carry our nuclear warheads played against us. The Russians, with no SAC, needed powerful missiles and this is what they developed. Later Soviet space achievements can be credited largely to their perfecting of rocket-propulsion devices with much greater thrust than ours. This has permitted them to·carry heavier payloads and more complex guidance equipment. (Another current Russian joke says: "The trouble with American satellites is that no one can find a dog small enough to go up in one.")

The Soviets completely by-passed small-scale rocket demonstrations such as our Vanguard series. Russian planning from the start called for an aggressive space program aimed at boosting significant experiments into space very early in the game. Even today, after several years of work, our largest available rocket booster — the Atlas — provides about one-half the estimated thrust of the Soviet first-stage rocket booster, and we have just begun to use the Atlas.

Why such a discrepancy in rocket thrust? Wernher von Braun has stated the reason in a few sentences: "The years between 1945 and 1951, during which the Russians laid the groundwork for their large rocket program, are irretrievably lost. The United States went into a serious ballistic missile program only in 1951 . . . Thus our present dilemma is not due to the fact that we are not working hard enough now, but that we did not work hard enough during the first six to 10 years after the war."

Russia's efforts paid off most handsomely on Oct. 4, 1957, when Sputnik I first spelled out across the heavens the pre-eminence of Soviet science in a language all the world could understand. By early 1960, the USSR had successfully launched three earth satellites and three space probes — with dramatic results. Two achieved earth-escape velocity, one hitting the moon, the other orbiting the sun. Their third space probe looped around the moon, took pictures of the previously unseen side of the moon's surface, and successfully returned these lunar pictures to earth.

During this same period, the United States successfully launched almost three times as many earth satellites and space probes. Although much smaller than the Soviet payloads, American efforts have gained steadily in both size and complexity. A picture-taking weather satellite, sent aloft in April, 1960, and an interplanetary probe named Pioneer V — which will fly closer to the sun than any other man-made satellite thus far and will explore the 26-million-mile gap between the orbits of earth and Venus — were both spectacular accomplishments for the United States.

It should be understood, however, that the number of satellites launched no longer has any significance; both Russia and the United States now have the knowledge and capacity to put an unlimited number of satellites into orbit. Thus, score-keeping is meaningless. The only legitimate yardstick that can be placed against the two space programs is the amount of new knowledge being obtained, and here the Soviets are without question in the lead.

Their ability to boost heavier probes into space has enabled them to achieve such dramatic firsts as sending animals into space, circling the sun, hitting the moon, and photographing the far side of the moon. The argument that miniaturization has enabled us to gather as much space knowledge with smaller payloads just doesn't ring true in the light of Soviet accomplishments.

But one particularly dramatic area, now attainable, is still open to competition between the two nations: *sending a man into space and then successfully recovering him.* The impact on the world of completing such a mission will undoubtedly be as profound — or more so — as was the firing of Sputnik I, the world's first satellite, in October, 1957.

The Russians have been very quiet about their man-into-space program. This gives them the opportunity for maximum dramatic effect if they carry the feat off successfully, and frees them of the necessity of reporting failures. And a number of scientists — particularly in Europe — are convinced that there have been failures. A report from Italy claimed that four Russians, a woman and three men, had died in efforts to orbit them. And West Germany's top rocket scientist, Hermann Oberth, said early in 1960: "I have known for months from American intelligence reports that Russia tried to launch a manned space satellite near the end of 1957 or the beginning of 1958." According to Oberth, a Russian astronaut named Alexej Ledowsky was launched into space in a rocket that failed to orbit, and the astronaut was killed.

A Soviet scientist issues last minute instructions to a Russian astronaut before he undergoes a "flight" in an altitude chamber to test an experimental space suit.

SEVEN INTO SPACE

Russian statements on manned space flight have been curiously contradictory. Shortly after the Russian lunar hit in September, 1959, Alexander Topchiev, vice president of the Soviet Academy of Sciences, predicted a manned space flight in "the not-too-distant future." In the same roseate glow of success, the head of the Moscow Astronomic Institute said: "A couple more flights like this one and we will be ready for perfectly safe manned space trips." Yet, only a few months later, Russian's top space official, Prof. Leonid Sedov, told reporters that a manned space flight is "not a thing to be done in the near future" — adding that although such flights are quite possible now, the Soviet Union won't risk human lives until there's "absolute safety for the pilot and we really have some task these men should perform that cannot be performed by automation."

University of Maryland physicist Dr. Fred Singer, after a three-month visit in Russia during 1959, came home convinced these moderating statements reflect some serious difficulties the Russians are experiencing in their man-into-space efforts — particularly in testing a man-carrying capsule and developing an adequate tracking system. "I had thought the Russians were much further ahead than I now think they are," said Dr. Singer. "Getting a man into space first will be a tight race."

About all that's known for sure is that the Russians definitely have a man-into-space program in which at least three Red Air Force pilots are being trained in much the same manner as the Mercury Astronauts in this country. The Soviets have the advantage of knowing the exact state of our man-into-space program. It can be presumed that they will make an earnest effort to launch an astronaut before we do. How many unsuccessful launchings will precede the first successful orbiting by a Soviet astronaut we'll probably never know. But at this writing, there is still a

A Soviet space team compares notes. A Russian test pilot, laboratory technician, and two scientists examine data on which the pilot's physiological reactions were recorded during a test.

profound silence from the Soviet Union on its man-into-space program.

* * *

The space challenge has not yet been crystallized in a way that Americans can understand. The Eisenhower Administration line has consistently been that we are not in a race with the Russians to put a man into space, and even the American Astronauts have been more-or-less faithfully following this line. (One of them told me flatly: "Definitely our objective in this program is not to beat the Russians.") If the Russians are more realistic on this point, perhaps it's because they have a somewhat lower capacity for kidding themselves. Even so, it's problematical if any of the Americans who are so earnestly espousing this viewpoint really believe it. But whether they believe it or not, the fact remains that we are most decidedly in a race with the Russians in space. And one area in which we still have an *immediate* chance of licking them is in our man-into-space program. This is the job of a talented and dedicated group of men brought together under the apt title of Project Mercury.

Although Project Mercury was officially initiated on Oct. 5, 1958, it had its genesis in research studies of a group of scientists in the National Advisory Committee for Astronautics. They had been deliberating for some time on the practicability of firing a capsule into orbit and then bringing it safely back to earth. When NASA moved into the picture in 1958, this project was transferred to the new space agency and labeled Project Mercury. It has two stated objectives:

(1) The study of human capabilities in the space environment;

(2) The study of system requirements necessary to sustain the launch, flight, and successful re-entry from orbital

speeds. In less bureaucratic language, Project Mercury has one very simple and specific responsibility: to put a manned satellite into orbit and recover the capsule and its astronaut safely. From the beginning, Project Mercury was the most exciting and dramatic phase of our space program. It still is.

Robert R. Gilruth, a 47-year-old scientist and engineer with a lifetime of profound accomplishments in the field of aerodynamics, was named to head up Project Mercury. The nucleus of his staff was selected from scientists at the Langley Research Center in Hampton, Va., where Project Mercury's headquarters were established late in 1958. It is perhaps symbolic that from this same Langley Field some 40 years ago, Gen. Billy Mitchell led his flight of aviators out over the Atlantic to sink an American battleship — and thus establish a new concept of warfare.

Once the purpose of Project Mercury had been delineated, the nucleus of a staff selected, and headquarters established, there was an immediate and urgent need to select the trainees around whom this whole program would evolve. Thus, on Jan. 27, 1959, it was announced that an undetermined number of young American men would be selected for space-flight training. The tests would be thorough and rigid and the requirements demanding. It was necessary that these men — probably more so than any other single group in history — represent the ultimate in engineering skill and training, physical stamina and well-being, psychological adaptability and desire, and flying experience and ability. This was a large order. Only a few could qualify. These would be the Mercury Astronauts — the men destined to carry the banner of the free world into space.

CHAPTER THREE

SELECTING
THE ASTRONAUTS

"It is a brazen conceit to suppose that a machine
can be built even one-half as capable as the
mind of man."

—*Scott Crossfield, X-15 test pilot*

On a steamy April afternoon in Washington, D. C. in
the year of the Space Age, 1959, an overflow crowd of
newsmen pushed into the small auditorium of a down-at-
the-heels three-story terra cotta building a few blocks from
the White House. A plaque beside the entrance told pass-
ers-by that this building housed the headquarters of America's National Aeronautics and Space Administration. It
wasn't — nor is it yet — an edifice calculated to inject fear
in the souls of any Soviet visitors snooping about to discover how seriously we're taking space exploration.

But in spite of the modest surroundings, a drama of high
importance was scheduled for its premiere performance
on the NASA stage. At precisely 2 o'clock on the afternoon
of April 9, 1959, the NASA press chief, Walter Bonney,
stepped on the stage. Behind him were seated seven re-

markably-at-ease young men dressed in business suits.

With a flourish that indicated more than a passing sensitivity to the momentousness of his announcement, Mr. Bonney said simply: "Gentlemen, these are the Astronaut volunteers."

Between the establishment of Project Mercury on Oct. 5, 1958, and the unveiling of the Astronauts the following April, were six months of frenzied activity. During that time, NASA officials had to decide what qualifications Astronauts should have, where such individuals might best be found, how they should be segregated and tested, how many should be included in the program, and how and by whom the final selection should be made.

There were no precedents to follow. No government procedures had been established for Astronauts. No ground rules existed for spacemen. This made the task both easier and more difficult — easier because second-guessing was reduced to a minimum; more difficult because there was little information on which to base even the most elementary decisions.

From the beginning, it was realized that there were three crucial criteria for selecting our first space trainees: technical, physical, and psychological. In the vast expanse of type that has been devoted to the Astronauts since their selection, the first prerequisite — technical training and competence — has been grossly underplayed.

Obviously many thousands of American men might have qualified physically and psychologically. Press notices to the contrary, the Astronauts have never been held up either as supermen or geniuses. They are remarkable physical and mental specimens; but so are a good many other American young men. Therefore the really crucial point on which their selection depended was technical competence.

Dr. Robert Voas, one of the Project Mercury psychologists, explained it to me this way: "We were looking for a professional group that already fulfilled many of the requirements necessary to enable us to achieve space flight *at the earliest time*. This brought us inevitably to test pilots. Others could undoubtedly have been trained, but these men had a tremendous head start in the most important factor of all — technical skill."

Limiting the field to experienced pilots was the first obvious step. It would be foolish — particularly in a semi-crash program — to train Astronauts in the basics of flying when a sizeable pool of trained pilots was available. But even this limitation left too unwieldy a group from which to winnow the final choices. And at no time was consideration given to throwing Project Mercury open to volunteers from among our considerable number of experienced pilots. Psychologists insisted, with some justification, that many of the men who would blindly volunteer to be fired into orbit would show signs of emotional instability. Thus it was determined to pre-select a rather small group from which volunteers would be sought after the program had been carefully explained to them.

The next step, therefore, was reaching into our pilot force and extracting the specialized group most likely to meet the qualifications for space adventure. Because many of the conditions expected in orbital flight are similar to those experienced almost daily by test pilots, the field was restricted to this group. Only one more step in the preliminary screening remained. There were about equal numbers of civilian and military test pilots. The selection of civilian test pilots presented some problems. In many instances it would be difficult to pry them away from their companies. The pay in the Mercury program would not be attractive to these men. Most of them were far enough removed from military life to make it difficult to condition

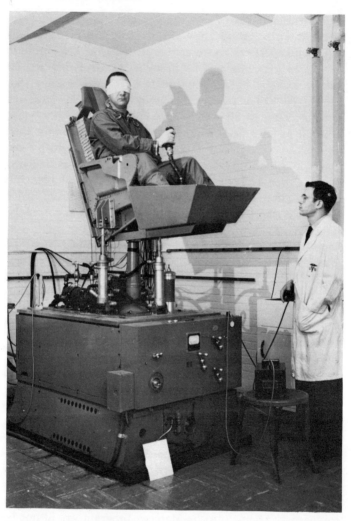

One of the most sensitive tests given the Astronauts was this rotating equilibrium chair. Gus Grissom demonstrates his skill at keeping it straight and level even while blindfolded.

them to the type of discipline contemplated for Project Mercury.

By contrast, military test pilots offered a number of peculiar advantages. They were available. (The military services had indicated willingness to cooperate with the man-in-to-space program.) They would suffer no financial loss. (If military pilots were selected, they were to be paid at their regular military pay rate.) They were adjusted to the rigors of military life. And their complete records were easily accessible to NASA authorities.

So it was decided, late in 1958, to restrict the search for America's first Astronauts to the military test pilots. Accordingly, records of all military test pilots were forwarded to NASA and were carefully reviewed.

"There were some arbitrary criteria in this initial screening," said Brig. Gen. Donald D. Flickinger, surgeon and assistant deputy commander for research of the Air Research and Development Command, "that had to do with educational background, height, previously administered intelligence tests, and medical-history background. The height limit of 5 feet 11 inches, for example, was irrevocable because it was governed by the dimensions within the space capsule."

To which Capt. Norman Barr, director of the Navy's Astronautical Division of Medicine and Surgery, added: "These men also had to have a technical background in the subjects related to this new specialty. They had to have about 1,500 hours as pilots of jet-type aircraft. They had to know some astronomy, physics, and other basic sciences. You can't find very many young men who have these qualifications."

This initial screening washed out more than three-fourths of the 400-plus military test pilots considered for the Mercury program. The principal eliminating factor was lack of sufficient technical experience. This left NASA brass, in January, 1959, holding the dossiers of 69 military test pilots who met the general qualifications set for the Astronauts. Now the selection must be on a very personal basis.

These men were brought singly to Washington and interviewed. The Mercury program was explained to them carefully, and their questions answered as fully as possible. Each candidate was then given the opportunity to drop from contention; some 80 percent elected to remain. After further personal consultations, the field of candidates was narrowed to 32 young men, all eager to become the free world's first emissaries into space.

At this point, it was decided to restrict the number of Astronauts to seven instead of the 12 originally contemplated. The most important reason for cutting the number was to give each Astronaut the opportunity for maximum participation in the Mercury program. These men were to be much more than pilots; they were to have an important part in planning the program, designing the equipment, and working out the technical problems that would arise. Since these problems were divided into seven major technical areas, it was decided that seven Astronauts should be trained, one to specialize in each problem area.

The final selection was a highly complicated medical, technical, and psychological contest. Says Dr. W. Randolph Lovelace, II, who headed up the medical and biological aspects of the Astronaut selection: "The Project Mercury candidates underwent one of the toughest medical examinations in history. We couldn't afford to overlook any test that might catch even a minor defect."

Immediately following their Washington interviews, the 32 remaining candidates were divided into six groups to report — one group at a time — to the Lovelace Clinic in Albuquerque, N. Mex. (selected partly for its geographical

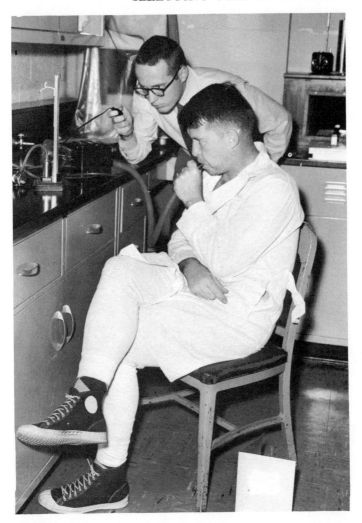

Wally Schirra eyes the recording device malevolently as his lung capacity is tested. The procedure involves taking a deep breath and exhaling it into the tube.

Scott Carpenter reads placidly as his ability to function under the stress of extreme heat is measured by Project Mercury doctors. The temperature in the heat chamber is 130°F.

isolation). The first contingent entered Lovelace on Feb. 7, and the others on succeeding Saturdays. Each candidate spent seven and one-half days undergoing tests at the Clinic.

Obviously these men, as professional test pilots — one of the most rigorous and demanding of all professions — were physically fit. It wasn't anticipated that any of the 32 would be disqualified as physically unfit, and none was. Thus the primary purpose of the physical examinations became comparative. Which of these men were the best of the best?

To answer this question, the men were put through a series of examinations almost devilish in their intensity. (Astronaut John Glenn said later: "I didn't know the human body had so many openings to explore.")

The testing began at 7 a.m., and frequently extended into the evening. There were 17 separate procedures in the eye examination. Almost 30 laboratory tests were made on each man. Brain waves were measured, and so was the specific gravity of each candidate's body (by strapping him in a chair and dunking him in a tankful of warm water — which turned out to be the most comfortable test of the entire session).

The Astronaut candidates had to pedal bicycles against increasing brake loads and lie in a cylindrical trough while body radiation was measured. Water was dripped into their ears to determine susceptibility to motion sickness and dizziness — factors which would prove decidedly uncomfortable, and possibly even fatal, in outer space.

They were shocked, prodded, and punctured unmercifully. Yet, it is symptomatic of the high motivation of these men that not one of the 32 missed a single appointment during the testing period. And only one of the candidates was medically disqualified — and then only temporarily for a minor and remediable defect.

After each group finished the week's examination, it had

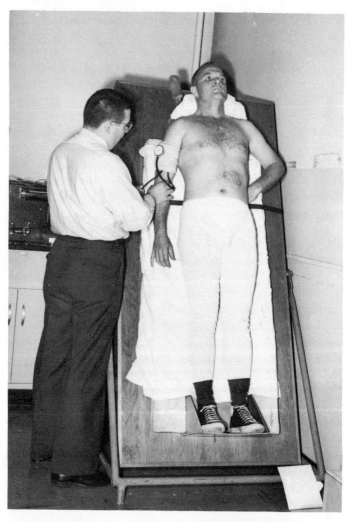

John Glenn reclines solemnly on a tilt table while his blood pressure is checked. This test measures the ability of the heart to function properly while the body is in this unusual position.

a few days to relax and paint grotesque pictures of the testing procedure for the incoming group. Then, those who had completed their medical examinations moved on to Dayton, Ohio for the next phase of the testing program.

Psychological and stress tests were given at the Wright Air Development Center in Dayton. The first group of prospective Astronauts entered WADC on Feb. 15; each man was evaluated for six days. There were 25 tests in the psychological area, alone. Said Dr. George E. Ruff, one of the psychiatrists supervising the testing: "We were particularly thorough here since we knew a journey into space will involve complexities and dangers that will tax a man's inner strength to the utmost."

The candidates were given all the standard psychological tests — ink blots, apperception (telling stories suggested by pictures), sentence-completion, self-inventory, and similar tests. They were also given a number of other tests peculiar to the business at hand.

For example:

The candidates were placed before a panel with 12 signals (called an "idiot box" by the pilots), each requiring a different response. They were then presented with a highly confusing situation and instructed to solve the problem by pressing the proper sequence of signals.

Each aspirant was isolated for three hours in a completely dark, absolutely soundless room to determine his ability to cope with the absence of external stimuli.

Candidates were subjected to a battery of sounds and sound frequencies to determine their susceptibility to noise.

In general — and in somewhat varying degrees — the 32 candidates were found to be well-integrated individuals with a mature psychological approach to hazardous and new types of experiences, which is precisely the attitude they would need to face the adventure awaiting them.

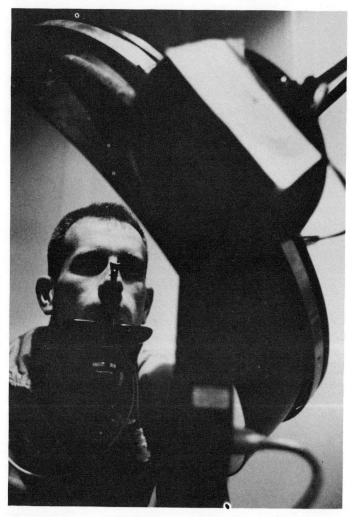

Deke Slayton seems to be looking beyond the eye test being given him after a ride in the centrifuge—one of the many tests given to the Project Mercury Astronaut candidates.

In addition to psychological tests, the candidates were also given a battery of "stress" tests at the Wright Air Development Center. Much information in this area was already available on them because of previous studies made before the candidates became test pilots. Thus the additional tests were tailored to meet specific requirements for orbital flight.

Under the heading of stress tests, the prospective Astronauts were required — among other things — to:

Maintain a constant pace on a treadmill being elevated one degree each minute — until the heart reached 180 beats per minute;

Step 20 inches to a platform once every two seconds for five minutes (if that sounds easy, try it);

Plunge warm feet into a tub of ice water while pulse and blood pressure were measured;

Withstand multiple gravity forces at various angles in a centrifuge;

Maintain a chair, which rotated on two axes, on an even keel with a control stick with and without vibration, normally and while blindfolded;

Spend two hours in a "bake chamber" with the temperature set at 130° F.

When it was all over, a tired Dr. Lovelace said with feeling: "I just hope *they* never give *me* a physical examination. It's been a long, rough period that they've been through. But when we can work with highly-motivated and intelligent men like these, it makes our job much easier."

Early in March of 1959, the results of all the tests were brought together in Washington. There, a half-dozen men — representing the most expert medical and technical judgment available — weighed and re-weighed the data. To them, the candidates were merely numbers. From the first day of the testing until the final selection, the 32 candidates were nameless to the people conducting and evaluating the examinations. Until the seven best qualified candidates were finally chosen, numbers were used for the names of the men being considered. On the first of April, 1959, orders went out to the chosen seven professional military test pilots to report to Langley Field, Va. for detached duty with the civilian space agency — to undergo training for manned space flight.

Thus was the U.S. space program — for the first time — put into terms the American public could understand. Space was humanized.

Before the selection of the Astronauts, there was an otherworldly feel to the whole idea of space exploration. Individual American citizens — whose support and understanding is essential in a governmental system such as ours — could find little to relate to in the space program. Then the Astronauts were named — seven very real and very human young men. All had wives, all had children. They were good-looking and personable — representing the cream of American physical and intellectual ability. All had IQ's in excess of 130; they ranged in age from 32 to 37; four were even named "Junior."

And all of them were willing — even eager — to risk being blasted into the frightening unknown of outer space.

Americans sat up and took notice. The Astronauts overnight became a household word. And millions of citizens — who had never before given a passing thought to outer space — began to ask each other: "Who are these Astronauts and why did they agree to a crazy thing like this?"

We can get an insight into the nature of these seven Astronauts from the results of the psychological testing they went through during the selection process. We learn, for instance, that:

They set themselves reachable, realistic goals without

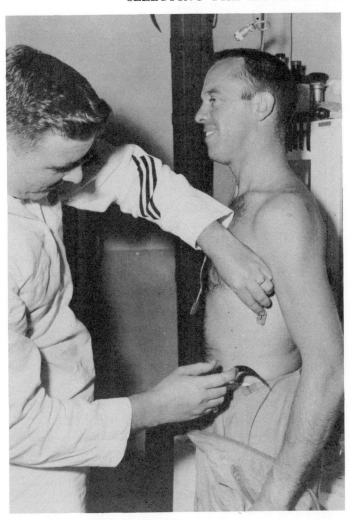

Alan Shepard seems to enjoy having the electrodes removed from his skin after they have supplied detailed medical information on his reactions to a strenuous stress test.

dwelling in a perpetual state of dreamland;

Although basically adventurous, they can do and accept routine tasks without frustration or fretting;

They adapt almost instantaneously to strange surroundings;

They plan skillfully and specifically for emergency action in every situation where the possibility of failure exists;

They don't act impulsively;

They get along well with people — but have no hesitation in taking action which puts them in conflict with others, when the action is called for. (During the weeks of testing, the 32 pilots under consideration enjoyed each other's company immensely during their free time, but competed like tigers during the day. All enjoyed beating their rivals, none showed the slightest guilt feelings about surpassing their comrades — and all of them competed strictly by the rules) ;

They are completely self-reliant and never seek help unless they need it. When they do need it, they have no hesitation about asking for it.

Let's meet the Astronauts now, just as they were first introduced to the American public from that stage in the NASA headquarters building on April 9, 1959.

* * *

JOHN H. GLENN, JR., born in 1921, is the oldest Astronaut. He is also the only Marine in the group. Because these self-reliant test pilots have little need of a father-image in their group, the occasion seldom arises when one of them is thrust forward as a "pappy guy." But when a question of general policy is posed to the group that falls in no man's specialty, Glenn is most frequently the Astronaut who will answer.

He's smooth, soft-spoken, amiable, and has a tendency to talk in the same sort of homilies so often heard from President Eisenhower. When the other Astronauts, for example,

become restive at the question of whether or not we're in a space race with the Russians, Glenn can still say: "This is a technological program, not a space race. Our primary concern is not to beat the Russians but to put a man up and bring him back safely."

Glenn is the best public relations man among the Astronauts. He also has the most extensive combat record in the group, is the most decorated, and was best known — before his selection as an Astronaut — for his flying achievements.

A native of Ohio, Glenn graduated from high school in New Concord in 1939. His father operated a plumbing and heating business, and his mother was the daughter of a local doctor. John was raised — with his sister, Jean — in comfortable, upper-middle class surroundings in a small Midwestern town. He was in his second year at Muskingum College when the United States declared war on Japan. (A back on the Muskingum football team, Glenn is the only Astronaut who engaged in any major varsity sports.)

Glenn enlisted in the naval aviation cadet program a few weeks after Pearl Harbor, and was called to active duty in March, 1942. In the midst of his training, he chose the Marine Corps over the Navy, and in March, 1943, he won his wings as a second lieutenant in the Marine Air Corps at Corpus Christi, Tex. As a member of Marine Fighter Squadron 155, he flew 59 combat missions against the Japanese in Corsairs from the Marshall Islands. Returning to the United States, he married Anna Margaret Castor — a hometown girl whom he had been courting since he was six years old. When the war ended, Capt. Glenn decided to make a career of the Marine Corps. His future was tied inextricably with the airplane; his choice was really whether to pursue his particular star as a civilian or military pilot, and he chose the latter.

After duty in China and Guam, Glenn spent a year and a half as a flight instructor at Corpus Christi, then attended Amphibious Warfare School at Quantico, Va. In Korea, he flew 90 combat missions, his duty being with both the Marines and the Air Force. He shot down three MIG's along the Yalu River in the last week of combat in Korea. As a result of his combat service in both World War II and Korea, Glenn has been awarded the Distinguished Flying Cross five times and the Air Medal with 18 Clusters.

Home from Korea, Maj. Glenn attended test-pilot school at Patuxent River, Md., then was assigned as project officer on a number of experimental Navy aircraft. During the two years immediately prior to his selection as an Astronaut, he was assigned to the Fighter Design Branch of the Navy Bureau of Aeronautics in Washington. He made headline news in 1957 when he set a transcontinental speed record of three hours, 23 minutes from Los Angeles to New York.

Now a lieutenant colonel, Glenn has more than 5,000 hours in the air, including 1,500 in jet aircraft. He's built like a fullback, medium height (5 feet, 10½ inches), stocky (he weighs 180 pounds) and powerful. His thinning reddish blond hair is close-cropped, his light-green eyes amiable and almost translucent, his grin infectious, his speech quiet and deliberate.

John and Anna Glenn have two children, John David and Carolyn (born in 1946 and 1947 respectively). They have a warm and close family relationship, built to a considerable extent on the strong religious convictions they all share.

"I'm a Presbyterian and take my religion very seriously," says Glenn. "I think you'll find a lot of pilots who look at their work from a fatalistic standpoint. They say: 'I'm going to die some time, so I can do anything I want in the meantime and it makes no difference because when my time comes, I'm going anyway.'

"This isn't what I believe. I was brought up to believe that we are placed here with certain talents and capabilities, and it's up to each of us to use them as best we can. If we do that, I believe there is a power greater than any of us that will place the opportunities in our way. That's how I look at this Mercury program. If I use the talents and capabilities I happen to have been given to the best of my ability, I think there is a power greater than I am that will certainly see that I am taken care of — as long as I live up to my part of the bargain."

Glenn works assiduously on his own at keeping in shape. He enjoys water sports and does a great deal of boating and water skiing with his family. In the summer of 1959, he also started a program of running two miles before breakfast, and has stuck with it in spite of ribbing from his less energetic colleagues.

Regarding Project Mercury, Glenn says earnestly:

"I think we're very fortunate to have been blessed with the talents that enabled us to be picked for something like this . . . I think each one of us would feel guilty if he didn't make the fullest use of them for something as important as Project Mercury is to our country and the world in general."

* * *

Leroy G. Cooper is the youngest of the Astronauts. Born in Oklahoma in 1927, he was too young for World War II, and was assigned to an Air Force squadron in Germany during the Korean fighting. Cooper is the only Astronaut with no combat experience.

At 5 feet 9 inches, Gordon Cooper looks taller because of his gangly appearance. His 150 pounds are well distributed on a wiry frame, and he seems all arms and legs when he

walks. He has the deliberate speech of the Westerner, and sounds and talks like one of the cowhands on his father's Colorado ranch. He's tenacious and can be stubborn concerning things about which he feels strongly.

Cooper's love of flying goes back to his early childhood. His father (now retired) was an Air Force career officer and pilot, and a friend of both Wiley Post and Amelia Earhart. Young Gordon was handling the controls of an airplane when he was eight years old, and flew solo when he was 16. With such a background, it's scarcely surprising that Cooper read science fiction and Buck Rogers comics as a child—and dreamed of the day when he might emulate his fictional heroes.

Cooper enlisted in the Marine Corps in 1945 after his graduation from high school in Shawnee, Okla. He was discharged the following year and enrolled at the University of Hawaii. There he met a young lady who shared his passion for flying. Trudy Cooper captured her husband on the wing; they met in a flying club and carried on their courtship in a Piper Cub over the island of Oahu.

Trudy and Gordon were married while he was still in school, and their oldest daughter, Camala, was indoctrinated in flying in Hawaii before she was a year old. Gordon had received a reserve officer's commission in the Army while he was in college. He transferred the commission to the Air Force in 1949, and was immediately called to active duty for military flight training. After receiving his Air Force wings, he was sent to Germany as an F-86 pilot with the 86th Fighter Bomber Group.

When Cooper returned home, he was enrolled at the Air Force Institute of Technology in Dayton, Ohio where he won a degree in aeronautical engineering. He then attended the Air Force Experimental Flight Test School, and was working with experimental aircraft at Edwards Air Force

Base in California when news reached him that he had been chosen as one of the Astronauts.

Cooper has the lean, rawboned appearance and the characteristic taciturnity of the western outdoorsman. His hobbies are riding, hunting, and fishing, and he often takes Trudy and their two daughters (Janita was born a year after Camala) on hiking expeditions. He wears his dark hair close cropped and prefers bow ties when he has to wear a tie. His 2,300 flying hours include about 1,400 in jets.

A lifelong Methodist, he thinks "religion is definitely a sustaining aid. Likewise," he adds, "I have faith in the people I'm working with in this program, and I know it will be a success. I think I'm motivated by the fact that I'm a career officer, career pilot — and this is something new and very interesting."

The fact that Capt. Cooper could refer to being shot into space as "interesting" illustrates not only his personal penchant for understatement but an attitude on the part of all the Astronauts not generally understood: that Project Mercury is merely an extension of the flight testing work in which all of them have been engaged for some years. With Gordon Cooper, it has been literally a lifetime labor of love.

* * *

DONALD K. SLAYTON is the image of the bold, dashing military pilot — in spite of his engineering background. Among the seven Mercury Astronauts, he probably most closely resembles — both in appearance and manner — the public's idea of what the adventurous, hell-for-leather space explorer should be.

Born in Wisconsin in 1924, Deke Slayton is 5 feet 10½ inches tall and weighs 160 pounds. His brown hair is receding a bit, but not too noticeably. His features are dominated by a pair of whimsical blue eyes that seem to say their

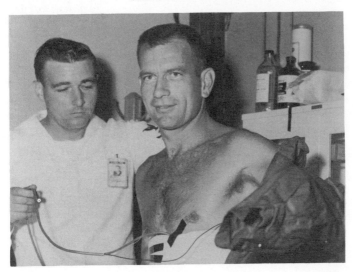

owner finds it difficult to take anything too seriously. Slayton is blunt and earthy, but also thoughtful. He doesn't wear his emotions on his sleeve, and his Scotch thrift shows up in economy of words.

The biographical facts point almost inevitably to Deke Slayton, Astronaut. He was raised in Sparta, Wis. with three brothers and two sisters in a comfortable small town environment. He enlisted in the Air Force as an aviation cadet as soon as he graduated from Sparta High School in 1942. During World War II, he flew 56 combat missions in B-25's in Europe and was awarded the Air Medal with Cluster. After a year as a flight instructor, he was sent to Okinawa and got in seven combat missions over Japan before the war ended — making him the only Astronaut with combat experience in both Europe and the Pacific during W. W. II.

After the war, Slayton entered the University of Minnesota and was graduated with a degree in aeronautical engineering in 1949. He then worked for Boeing Airplane until he was recalled to active duty with the Air Force during the Korean War. This time, he elected to make a career of military flying, and in 1953 he was assigned to the 36th Fighter Day Wing in Germany.

There he met a lively dark-haired California girl named Marjorie Lunney, who was working as a secretary for the U.S. Air Force in Berlin. They were married in 1955, honeymooned in Paris, then returned to the United States so Deke could attend test-pilot school at Edwards Air Force Base in California. Like Gordon Cooper, Capt. Slayton was testing experimental jet aircraft at Edwards when he was notified of his selection as an Astronaut. He has 3,400 flying hours — 2,000 in jets.

The Slaytons have one child — three-year-old Kent. Like the other Astronaut families, their hobbies are principally outdoor activities — especially hunting, fishing, and skiing.

Slayton can often be found wearing a sport shirt when the other Astronauts are in coat-and-tie. He has the endurance of a rhino (he set a record on the treadmill during the testing program) and frequently flies high-powered jet aircraft without a G-suit (he pulled 9.2 G's before blacking out in the tests). He has a remarkable learning potential and an IQ approaching genius. And he wants very much to be the first man in orbit.

"I don't feel that any particular extra faith is called for in this program over what we normally have," says Deke Slayton. "This is just a natural extension of flight. We've gone about as far as we can on this globe, so we'll have to start looking around a bit. I feel I'm in on the ground floor of something human beings will be concentrating on for the next thousand years — if we don't destroy ourselves in the meantime."

VIRGIL I. GRISSOM's sleepy-eyed appearance belies his 15 years of air-adventuring. The shortest of the Astronauts (5 feet 7 inches) Gus Grissom is quiet and almost diffident in conversation. He looks like the Boy Scout leader down the block, and is probably — along with John Glenn and Scott Carpenter — the most even-tempered of the Astronauts. His cropped brown hair has just the suggestion of a cowlick, and his brown eyes are quiet, assured, and a little bemused.

Grissom was born in 1926 in Mitchell, Ind. And, like the other Astronauts, he enjoyed a pleasant, comfortable, small-town upbringing. His wife, Betty, is also from Mitchell; she and Gus grew up together.

In Grissom's case, too, the career pattern is familiar. He went directly from high school into flight training (in 1944), but he was discharged from the Air Force at war's end before he had won his wings. There followed four years

at Purdue University, a degree in mechanical engineering, and a return to the Air Force to complete his flight training. By that time, Gus and Betty were married and had their first son, Scott. (Mark came along four years later.)

Grissom received his wings in 1951 and was sent almost immediately to Korea where he flew 100 combat missions in an F-86. A tour of duty as a flight instructor and study at the Air Force Institute of Technology preceded his enrollment in October, 1956, at test-pilot school. He was testing fighter planes at Wright-Patterson AFB when he switched over to space travel via Project Mercury. Two-thirds of Capt. Grissom's 3,000 air hours have been in jets, and he was awarded the Distinguished Flying Cross and Air Medal with Cluster for his combat work in Korea.

Getting into flying was probably a tougher struggle for Grissom than for any of the other Astronauts. Twice after World War II ended, Gus turned to a career in business, but he was desperately unhappy at it, and his wife encouraged him to return to flying. It was difficult after four years of financial struggle in college for the three Grissoms to face more of the same on the meager pay of an aviation cadet.

But this was the road that had to be traveled to reach the goal Gus had set for himself, and he has never regretted it. Oddly enough, one of the few air accidents in which any of the Astronauts have been involved took place when two of them were flying together. Several years ago, Grissom and Gordon Cooper demolished a T-33 on a take-off, but neither was hurt.

Gus was almost washed out of the Astronaut selection because of chronic hay fever. But he argued that there would be no ragweed in outer space, and apparently won his point. His reserved manner in no way indicates any lack of confidence in his own ability. It does, however, sometimes hide a sharp sense of humor.

"My career has been serving the country," he says, "and Project Mercury is another situation in which my talents can be used. I'm just grateful for the chance. I have great faith in the people who are working with us."

* * *

ALAN B. SHEPARD, JR. has followed the route of a professional military man — prep school, Annapolis, and sea duty aboard a destroyer in World War II. It wasn't until after the war that Shepard became a pilot instead of a deck officer.

Al Shepard is the fun-loving Astronaut, the practical joker — and usually the leader in any hanky-panky that takes place. He's ebullient and outspoken. He has a tendency to be impulsive and impatient. (He paid for civilian pilot instruction in his spare time while he was going through Navy flight training, because things were moving too slowly to

suit him.) He's seldom at a loss for words, and usually speaks quickly and enthusiastically — somewhat surprising in view of his New England background.

A slim 160-pounder, Lt. Comdr. Shepard stands just under six feet. An unusually high forehead and elongated nose give the impression of a long, thin face which makes his generous mouth and full lips stand out even more — like a good-natured guppy. His eyes are blue, and his brown hair is worn in a crew cut.

Shepard was born (in 1923) and raised in East Derry, N.H., where his father, a retired Army officer, is now an insurance broker. Shepard met his wife, Louise, while he was attending Annapolis, and they were married after his graduation.

Following wartime duty as a deck officer on the destroyer *Cosgrove,* Shepard entered Navy flight training in 1946 and won his wings a year later. After several tours of sea duty with a Navy fighter squadron, Shepard was sent to test-pilot school at Patuxent River, Md. Since that time he has alternated between test-flying some of the Navy's hottest aircraft and sea duty with a night fighter squadron flying jets.

Shepard was graduated from the Naval War College in 1958 and assigned to the staff of the commander-in-chief, Atlantic Fleet, as aircraft readiness officer. He was serving in this important post when he was selected for the Astronaut program — an assignment he wanted badly in spite of the obviously bright future ahead of him in the sea-going Navy. He has 3,600 hours in the air, about half in jets.

Al and Louise Shepard have two daughters, Laura, 12 and Juliana, 8. They all like water sports and ice skating — and Al also enjoys golf. Louise Shepard is a Christian Scientist, and Al attends this church regularly. He looks on Project Mercury as "merely one step in the evolution of space travel."

"The risk," he adds, "isn't as great as many people feel that it is. The men connected with this project won't attempt space flight until we reach the high probability that has been set. We have a better chance of coming back with the capsule than in many of our duties on routine flight tests in which we have been serving."

* * *

MALCOLM S. CARPENTER has the least flying experience in souped-up aircraft among the seven Astronauts. Of his 2,800 flying hours, only 300 are in jets. Although Carpenter enlisted in the Navy as an aviation cadet after he completed high school in 1943, the war ended in the midst of his flight training, and six years passed before he picked it up again — finally gaining his Navy wings in April, 1951.

In between these periods of flight training, Scott Carpenter returned to his home town of Boulder, Colo. (where he

was born in 1925), earned a degree in aeronautical engineering at the University of Colorado, and married his high school sweetheart, blonde René Price.

After his graduation from college, Carpenter re-joined the Navy, won his wings, attended the Fleet Airborne Electronics Training School in San Diego, and was assigned to a transitional training squadron for multi-engine Navy flying boats. He stayed with the large planes through most of his Navy flying career — the only Astronaut who specialized in multi-engine aircraft.

Carpenter was with a Navy patrol squadron in Hawaii when the Korean fighting started. He was sent to the combat area for anti-submarine and mining activities. In 1954, he returned to Patuxent River, Md. for test-pilot school. After several years of flight-testing Navy aircraft, Carpenter was enrolled in the Navy Air Intelligence School, then assigned to a non-flying job as air intelligence officer of the *USS Hornet*. He was preparing to go to sea when word came that he had been chosen for the final round of testing in the Astronaut selection program.

In size, Carpenter resembles Alan Shepard almost exactly — same height, weight, and structure. But there the resemblance ends. Carpenter's features are precise and finely-chiseled, his brow slightly furrowed, his demeanor thoughtful. His normal expression is one of quiet amusement or thoughtful consideration. He's polite, soft-spoken but incisive, somewhat reserved. He gives an impression of competence, self-assurance, and intelligent appraisal.

The Carpenters have four children — two girls and two boys, ranging in age from four to 11. They are very close as a family, and frequently discuss Scott's work together. Like the other Astronaut families, the Carpenters prefer water sports as their favorite outdoor activity — particularly water skiing and skin diving.

Of Project Mercury, Scott Carpenter says: "I know if there is anyone who can do a job like this, I can do it if I'm given the chance. It gives me the opportunity to use all my capabilities and interests at once. It's a chance to serve the country in a noble cause and to pioneer on a really grand scale. I'm happy and proud to be part of it. My sustaining faith is the fact that I believe we have the best minds in the country behind this project."

* * *

WALTER M. SCHIRRA (SHI-RAH), JR., comes from a noted flying family. His father (now a civil engineer with the Air Force in Hawaii) was a World War I ace and spent several years after the war barnstorming in a light plane (accompanied by his wife) before settling down to a military career.

Wally, who was born in 1923, and his sister were raised in

New Jersey, and he was graduated from Dwight Morrow High School in Englewood in 1940. After a year at the Newark College of Engineering, Schirra won an appointment to the United States Naval Academy, from which he was graduated as an ensign in 1945.

After several years of sea duty, Schirra's request for flight training was approved, and he won his Navy wings at Pensacola. As an exchange pilot with the 154th Air Force Fighter-Bomber Squadron, he flew 90 combat missions in F-84's in Korea — winning the Distinguished Flying Cross and two Air Medals.

Back from Korea, he helped develop the Sidewinder missile and the F-7U-3 Cutlass before a tour of aircraft carrier duty took him back to the Pacific. Home from two years at sea, he enrolled in the Navy test-pilot school and stayed at Patuxent River after completion of the course to take part in testing work on the F4H. Recently promoted to lieutenant commander, he had logged 3,000 hours — well over half of them in jets — when he was tapped for duty as an Astronaut.

Schirra's wife, the former Josephine Fraser of Seattle, Wash., has family military connections, too. She's the stepdaughter of Admiral James Holloway, former commander-in-chief of the Northeastern Atlantic and Mediterranean area. The Schirra's have two children, Walter III, 9, and Suzanne, 2.

On the beginnings of Project Mercury, Wally Schirra recalls: "I was reluctant to take part in what at first sounded like a stunt. But I gradually became convinced that this was a solid program and that really good test pilots were needed to handle the job. None of us is interested in the glamor of being a spaceman. We're interested in getting up and getting back. We have faith in the Space Age and in the people running this program. And we're interested in *new* things. Aviation was once new, but now it's 50 years old. So now we're expanding in another dimension."

Schirra talks like that — frank, straight-from-the-shoulder, sometimes blunt, often stubborn. He looks a little like a grown-up version of Alfalfa in the old Our Gang Comedies. His face is freckled, his complexion ruddy, and he seems to have a perpetual gee-whiz look about him. He's the only one of the Astronauts to wear his hair long — parted a little carelessly on the right side of his head. Like Glenn and Slayton, Wally Schirra is stocky and powerfully built, with 185 pounds well distributed over his 5-foot 10-inch frame.

"The space program," says Wally Schirra, "will have problems in it. But any man with pride in himself couldn't help but want to be the first man to look at the earth from up there."

To which at least six other Americans are willing to say "Amen."

These, then, are the Mercury Astronauts. From among them will come the free world's first man in space.

* * *

It would be silly to try — as some of the publicity men attached to them have — to pass the Astronauts off as "regular guys." They aren't. They're highly irregular. The mere fact that they have not only the capability but the desire to pioneer in space sets them apart. But even beyond this, these seven highly-individualistic men deserve more understanding treatment than to be anointed with the democratic kiss-of-death as "one of the boys." If this means being socially well-adjusted, they are that. But if it means substituting conformity for discrimination and thoughtfulness, they certainly don't qualify. The Astronauts are individuals in the most hallowed and independent American tradition.

It is hoped that these brief biographical sketches have humanized these unusual men a bit. They've been lionized so frequently — and yet so superficially — in the nation's press as to reduce them almost to a single lump of stoic heroism. It is unfair to them as individuals and untrue to any legitimate likeness simply to bunch them all together as representing America's greatest physical, intellectual, and technical ability — *in combination.* Yet, a good case can be made for this, too.

For every individual eccentricity in which the Astronauts differ, they are alike in a dozen ways. Some of their likenesses are curious. For example, all of them were raised in small towns . . . all had at least one brother or sister . . . all are Protestants . . . none came from impoverished homes . . . a majority have either parents or in-laws or both who made a career of military service . . . none of the Astronauts smoke (four did when the program started but have since quit voluntarily) . . . all are strongly motivated and self-confident without being self-centered or egotistical . . . all are in superb physical condition (one awed co-worker told me about seeing Carpenter effortlessly climb a 20-foot rope hand-over-hand in a friend's yard and watching Cooper lift 50-pound weights almost casually) . . . and all are mature, thoughtful, and intelligent men.

But the most obvious trait the Astronauts share is a deep-seated and delightful sense of humor. They manage to keep both themselves and their program in perspective, and this means they're able, frequently, to laugh at themselves. They have posted on the bulletin board in their office a magnificent cartoon showing the Astronauts all energetically doing pushups at Cape Canaveral while the project director rubs his chin and tries to decide which one will go first. The same bulletin board is cluttered with calendar art of nude women. The pictures have thoughtfully been located beneath a wall map; whenever photographs are being taken in the office or women visitors are present, the map is pulled down so it covers the bulletin board. Interchange between the Astronauts and the people with whom they work is informal, easy-going, and larded with humor.

Sometimes it comes unexpectedly — as witness a recent impulse of Scott Carpenter. After training flights on the centrifuge (which whirls them about at supersonic stresses), the Astronauts are kept under close medical observation for several hours because doctors are afraid of residual effects. The Astronauts know this, of course. Carpenter had just been examined after a training flight and the thermocouples removed from his skin. He took a shower, and when he returned to the examination room to dress, he noticed the medics huddled together paying no attention to him. Quietly he laid his towel on the concrete floor, then sprawled out on it as if he'd collapsed. The effect was well worth the trouble. The doctors almost had a collective stroke when they saw him — particularly since Carpenter seemed to them the least likely of the Astronauts to try such a gag.

Capt. Barr, U.S.N., summed up the feelings of those who helped select and now work with the Astronauts when he said: "I'm quite sure that no finer group of men could have been selected by the tests available to us today. These men have been chosen from a population of 180 million to represent the United States in this important project. All of us are very sure the correct men have been selected. We're behind them 100 percent."

So are the families of the seven Astronauts. It had to be that way. John Glenn was speaking for all the Astronauts when he said: "I don't think any of us could go on with something like this if we didn't have good backing at home."

Perhaps, someday, 180 million Americans will be for it, too. In the meantime, the chosen seven are hard at work — learning how to be Astronauts.

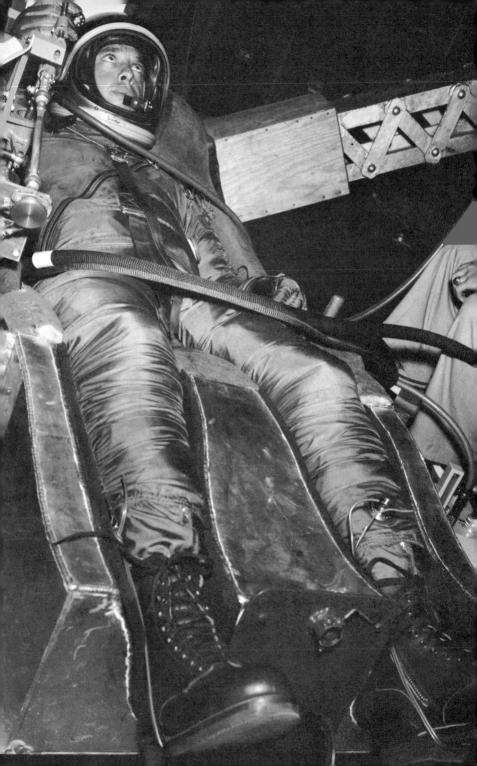

CHAPTER FOUR

TRAINING
THE ASTRONAUTS

"This project is comparable to the Wright brothers at Kitty Hawk, with Orville and Wilbur pitching a coin to see who was going to shove the other one off the hill. I think we stand on the verge of something as big and expansive as that was 50 years ago."

—Lt. Col. John Glenn, USMC

During the week I spent tagging the Astronauts through their training program, we took some photographs in the NASA cafeteria. As we were leaving, a woman worker stopped me and asked curiously: "Who were those men you were photographing?"

"The Mercury Astronauts," I told her.

She looked blank, said "Oh," and turned away. She had been employed there since the offices were opened and still didn't recognize the Astronauts, already several months into their training program.

This incident happened at the Astronauts' home base at Langley Field, Va. It is offered here only to illustrate the point that there is no three-ring circus going on at Langley. The fact that the Astronauts' ultimate goal is to be shot up into space sets their work apart considerably in the minds of outsiders. They accept this as part of the job, and are unflinchingly patient with inquirers. But, in general, they go about their daily tasks as prosaically as if they were posting books or selling meat at the corner grocery. They're fascinated with the job and sometimes even excited about it — but never breathless.

The Astronauts' training program is designed to do three things: (1) Work out the engineering and tactical bugs in the man-into-space program; (2) Develop, test, and modify the space hardware to the point of 99-percent reliability; (3) Train the Astronauts for space flight.

Most training programs are dreary to the trainee and boring to the reader. Project Mercury — over and above the exciting purpose toward which it is aimed — is out of this pattern for several reasons.

First, probably never before in history has a flight vehicle

The Astronauts' office quarters at Langley Field are certainly not plush. Here, five of the seven study the technical reports which are an important part of the training program.

and the means of propelling it been developed concurrently with the training of the men who will operate it.

Second, there have been no precedents to guide NASA in setting up its training program. And since no one has ever experienced space flight, the reactions of a man and vehicle in the space environment can only be guessed at.

And, third, the trainees, themselves, have an integral part in designing both the space hardware and the training program.

The focal point of the Astronauts' training activities is Langley Field, Va.—a large, staid and substantial-looking Air Force base in the red brick and ivy tradition, nestled on the southern tip of Virginia. NASA presently occupies a modest two-story building which is almost lost in the maze of Langley's permanent Air Force facilities.

The space agency quarters are certainly of this world. Scientists are grouped together in tiny offices; training equipment is crammed into a back room and the overflow stored in inaccessible corners of the nearby Langley Research Center; the Astronauts share one large, unpartitioned office. But the spirit of the place dominates the unimpressive surroundings. It is well illustrated by the pert blonde receptionist who sometimes answers the telephone with: "This is Space!" The facilities may be inadequate, but the Project Mercury team has still managed to keep its thinking out of this world.

The Astronauts are based at Langley Field about half of the time. They spend the rest visiting various installations around the country, conferring on the construction of space equipment and using training facilities not available at Langley.

During the time I was with them, their mornings were taken up with lectures and briefings, and their afternoons with flight simulators, proficiency flying, conferences with engineers and scientists on problems in each man's special area, and some exercise to keep in shape. Beyond the normal working day, the Astronauts' time is their own, and they live a reasonably normal life with their families. Two of the Astronauts — Cooper and Carpenter — live on the base at Langley. Glenn still maintains a home in Washington, D.C. and commutes on week-ends. Shepard lives about an hour's drive away at Virginia Beach, and Grissom, Schirra, and Slayton live in a new subdivision near Langley Field.

The training of the Astronauts breaks down into seven rather specific areas of activity. Let's examine them briefly.

(1) *Education in the Basic Sciences.* Two of the principal activities of the Astronauts — consulting on the design and construction of space equipment and learning how to make detailed scientific observations when they are launched into space — require a thorough grounding in the basic sciences. Consequently, a great deal of their time is spent in "school" — studying basic astronautics, physics, astronomy, propulsion, biophysics, gyroscopic theory, meteorology, and similar scientific and often highly-technical subjects.

The Astronauts comprise probably the smallest and most exclusive group of students in the nation — and employ the most expensive set of teachers. The lectures are delivered to them by the top scientists in the country. This is one reason Project Mercury is located at Langley Field. Scientists from the Langley Research Center are available to tutor the Astronauts.

As they approach the space-flight stage, the lecture portion of their training is being cut down considerably. Presently, the Astronauts have lectures only on specified mornings — when they're at Langley Field. At the same time, however, they are being supplied with a growing number of technical reports which they are expected to study and assimilate — in the few leisure moments they can find.

By the time the first space capsule is launched, each Astronaut will have completed enough classwork to qualify for a master's degree in the sciences.

(2) *Familiarization with the Conditions of Space Flight.* The duplication of space-flight conditions necessary for the training of the Astronauts has been a real problem to NASA officials. Training devices had to be created almost from scratch, and there was only limited knowledge to guide them. Much still remains to be done in this area.

The majority of the simulators — the name given training devices that approximate the conditions of space flight — are located at Langley Field. The most complex, a Buck Rogerish machine designed by NASA scientist Harold Johnson, simulates orbital flight motion. The device looks like the frame of a small automobile and is suspended in mid-air before a circular motion picture screen. The films, which the Astronaut sees through a periscope, are taken from the nose of a missile 100 miles up. To this extent, at least, the simulator is very real indeed. To practice tracking and navigation control, the Astronaut reclines on a couch, and in reference to a projected picture of the earth, makes attitudinal and navigational corrections. This machine "floats" on a powerful air jet, and smaller jets — controlled by the Astronaut — change the attitude of the trainer.

Another practice device is tucked away in a corner of a wind tunnel at the Langley Research Center. This one combines the Mercury capsule control panel with a stationary F-100 trainer. Flight control problems, fed into it from a computer across the street, give the Astronauts valuable training.

Still another simulator requires the Astronaut, by means of a hand control, to keep a ball-bearing centered on a

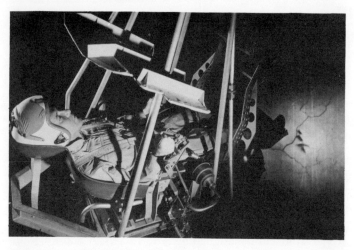

Wally Schirra practices orbital flight on the air-bearing simulator. Looking through the periscope overhead, he sees a projected picture of the earth on which he tracks his position.

flat metal disc which is being subjected to shifting and varying air currents. I tried this one, time after time, only to see the ball tumble almost instantly off the disc. Scott Carpenter stepped up behind me and held it, with scarcely a quiver, in dead center. It will take this sort of nerveless control to make the fine adjustments required to correct the flight of a capsule hurtling through space at 17,400 m.p.h.

Several major training devices take the Astronauts away from Langley Field. The most important — located at the Navy's Aviation Medical Laboratory in Johnsville, Pa.—is a Space-Age Link Trainer called a centrifuge. Here are duplicated acceleration stresses that the Astronauts will face in space flight. The trainee is strapped into a cockpit, faced with a battery of complicated instruments, and whirled and tumbled about to give him a taste of the acceleration strains he'll feel going up and coming down in the Mercury cap-

It takes a cool head and a steady hand—as exhibited here by Scott Carpenter—to keep the metal ball centered on the flat plate while it's buffeted by varying air currents.

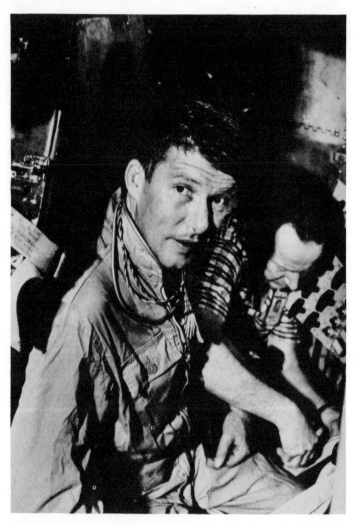

Wally Schirra—who probably took more "G's" than any man alive when the centrifuge ran wild on him—looks up quizzically as he's buckled into the centrifuge for another ride.

sule. During the launch and re-entry trajectories, the Astronaut-pilot will have to take about 8.6 "G's" (that is, about eight and one-half times the normal force of gravity). The duration of these peak "G's" will be only a fraction of a second, but the Astronaut will probably be above 5 "G's" for a half-minute to a minute. On the centrifuge, the Astronauts not only learn the sensations of extreme stress, but also how to manipulate control levers under these difficult conditions.

Occasionally the conditions become more demanding than even the Astronauts bargain for. Wally Schirra probably took more "G's" — and lived — than any man in history during one training flight on the centrifuge. The machine is supposed to build up stresses gradually, in response to data fed into it by an operator. But one day, with Schirra at the controls, it ran wild — whirling and tumbling the Astronaut in a malevolent frenzy of freedom. By the time someone pulled the plug, Schirra had experienced several minutes of the wildest ride imaginable. He emerged grinning — from an experience that could easily have killed him.

An observer told me: "These guys never seem to get shook up."

In this instance, the doctors who were standing by were in a much worse emotional state than Schirra.

At Wright Air Development Center in Dayton, Ohio and at Edwards Air Force Base in California, the Astronauts are exposed to the opposite effect, the absence of gravity — or weightlessness — that they will experience during orbital flight. The effect of sustained periods of weightlessness is one of the most critical unknowns facing the space adventurers. The best that can be done, at the moment, to reproduce it, is with two very different airplanes — the C-131 transport and the F-100 fighter. Each type of aircraft is put into a steep power dive, followed by an equally abrupt

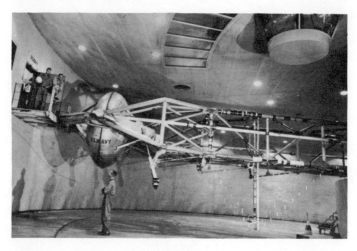

The Navy's giant centrifuge at Johnsville, Pa., is the principal training device of the Astronauts, whirling them about in a close approximation of the acceleration stresses of space flight.

climb. At the top of the climb, the plane pulls free of gravity, the C-131 for 15 seconds, the F-100 for about 45 seconds. During this brief period, any objects inside the plane that are not fastened down (including men) float free and weightless. Obviously this isn't enough time to study thoroughly man's reactions and capabilities during the weightless condition, but it's the best we can do at the moment.

Other simulators have been tried and abandoned. One such proposal entailed attaching a capsule to a balloon and sending it aloft to 100,000 feet. With each unsuccessful attempt to simulate weightlessness, it is becoming increasingly apparent that only after one of the men has actually experienced space flight and returned can any realistic training devices be created.

(3) *Aviation Flight Training.* Each of the Astronauts attached a condition to acceptance of the Mercury assign-

The Astronauts—floating freely about the cabin—are able to experience the sensations of weightlessness for about 15 seconds at a time in the cargo compartment of a C-131 transport.

ment: that during the training program he be permitted to maintain his proficiency in conventional aircraft. Accordingly, two F-102's have been assigned by the Air Force to the exclusive use of the Astronauts at Langley Field. Each man strives to put in at least 20 air hours a month. Much of this flying is done in pressure suits to help them adapt to long periods in this cumbersome gear. All of the Astronauts complain they don't get enough time in the air. Above all, these men are dedicated pilots. They love to fly, and look forward eagerly to leaving the classroom and the demands of space training for the flight line.

(4) *Participation in the Vehicle Development Program.* Wally Schirra told me: "There's always a certain amount of conflict between designers and engineers, and the men who are going to fly the machines. We've had a little of that here, too, but we're lucky on two counts. We've been

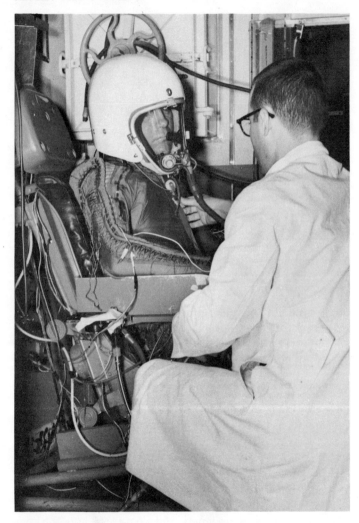

Deke Slayton prepares to go to an altitude of 65,000 feet in the Wright Air Development Center's altitude chamber to test his bodily reaction to a low-pressure environment.

able to work well with the technical people building the hardware, and we've had a chance to get our opinions registered at the design level. That doesn't happen very often to a pilot. But in this case, one of our most important jobs is to put the pilots' ideas into the cockpit of the capsule. After all, the engineers won't be going up into space with us."

Working with the people who are designing and building the Mercury equipment means a great deal of traveling for the Astronauts, for these companies are located all over the nation. There are three principal ports of call: McDonnell Aircraft of St. Louis, which is building the Mercury capsule; Convair, which builds the Atlas missile in San Diego; and the Rocketdyne Division of North American Aviation in Los Angeles.

Occasional group trips are also necessary to Huntsville, Ala. where the Redstone missiles are built, to Akron, Ohio where the Goodrich Company is manufacturing the space-flight suits, and to Cape Canaveral to be briefed on activities directly related to Project Mercury. The Astronauts have observed several Atlas firings — one of them the "Big Joe" test in which two of the rocket engines failed to drop off, causing the missile to wander far off course. They accepted this impassively.

"The Atlas will have the bugs worked out of it by the time we're ready to use it," said Deke Slayton, in whose specialty the Atlas falls.

And the chances are that this will be accomplished before the bugs are worked out of a much more prosaic problem — the Astronauts' earthbound traveling facilities. On a recent trip to Cape Canaveral, the Astronauts took a commercial airliner from Newport News, Va. to Washington, transferred to another airliner which carried them to Orlando, Fla., then completed the journey by rented automobile.

The author talks with Wally Schirra and Scott Carpenter before they take off from Langley Field on a practice flight in the two F-102's assigned to the Astronauts by the Air Force.

They took the same tortuous route back to Langley Field — sometimes spending hours hanging around airports awaiting flights. This same situation prevails in all of their travels. It stems from the fact that there are no funds available in the NASA budget to maintain an aircraft for the transportation of the Astronauts. The Air Force is willing to provide the aircraft — but not the maintenance. This bureaucratic nonsense probably costs the Astronauts several dozen working days a year. One of the Astronauts actually made a survey showing that both time and money could be saved by using a chartered aircraft. It's difficult, indeed, to imagine our top government officials permitting such a situation to exist in a program where we ought to be giving everything we have to catch up with the Russians.

In addition to group trips, the Astronauts make a number of individual visits in connection with their own technical specialties and give verbal reports to the others when they return. Thus each individual Astronaut is kept fully informed on the activities in every area of Mercury operations.

(5) *Physical Training Program.* Probably no aspect of the Astronauts' training is less understood than their physical conditioning program. The fact is that they simply don't have a formal program of diet or exercise. When Project Mercury started, the Astronauts were asked if they wanted regular calisthenics. Being experienced military men, they said "No" emphatically, and that was that. Their only group physical training has been a course with Navy frogmen, which ended with the Astronauts swimming a thousand yards under water using an aqualung and flippers.

This is not to say that they don't stay in good physical condition. But as Scott Carpenter pointed out: "We don't need any formal health or physical conditioning program. We're big boys now, and know how to take care of ourselves. Besides, this thing is important to us, and we're not

Infrequently, the Astronauts go in a group to Cape Canaveral to observe launchings. Here, all except Schirra cluster before an Atlas
gantry from which they will one day be launched.

going to let ourselves get out of shape."

All of the Astronauts enjoy water sports particularly, and indulge in them whenever possible. At the start of the program, four (Slayton, Shepard, Carpenter, and Schirra) smoked. Now, all of them abstain — but strictly on their own and under no duress. (The Astronauts' office at Langley has a hand-lettered sign stuck to the door which reads: NO SMOKING IN THIS ROOM PLEASE, and it's signed, "Four Ex-Smokers.")

According to Carpenter, there were two prime reasons for quitting cigarettes. First, some of the smokers came out of the centrifuge coughing. Second, there can be no smoking in the capsule, and it seemed foolish to add to the complications of space flight with cravings that couldn't be satisfied.

It's typical of the strong will and high motivation of

The only formal program of physical conditioning undergone by the already-fit Astronauts was a course in skindiving taught to them by Navy frogmen.

these men that once they decided to quite smoking, they simply stopped — and that was that. The press officer attached to the Astronauts — Col. John Powers — remembers the precise moment. In October, 1959, at the Los Angeles Airport, the four Astronauts who smoked stuffed their cigarettes in Powers' coat pocket as they boarded the plane— and none of them smoked again.

Being a test pilot is a rigorous profession. The Astronauts had to be in top physical condition to ply their trade, and they still are. But they get a little testy about the physical superlatives sometimes ascribed to them. John Glenn told me: "Sometimes I think people expect us to sprout wings and take off. This business of us being the greatest physical specimens in captivity is badly overstated. We're as healthy as any group you could find, but we aren't supermen. There are plenty of other people just as healthy."

To make sure they stay that way, Air Force Lt. Col. Bill Douglas has been assigned exclusively to the Astronauts as their flight surgeon. Without question, he presides over the healthiest group of any M.D. in the country.

(6) *Training in the Operation of the Mercury Vehicle.* From the beginning of heavier-than-air flight, pilots have been taught how to fly by actually handling the controls of an aircraft in flight. Obviously, this would also be the most effective way to learn to fly a space capsule. As a matter of fact, it seems to be the only way to overcome two serious deficiencies in the Mercury training program.

The first of these is the inability of scientists to reproduce weightlessness for a long enough period of time to provide the Astronauts any real indication of how they will react to this state when they're in space. The few seconds of free tumbling possible in a high-performance aircraft is more of a curiosity than a training aid.

The second problem is the lack, so far, of a comprehensive trainer — that is, one in which all, or at least a majority, of the flight problems to be encountered in space can be reproduced. The present simulators tackle only one problem at a time, and the Astronauts have no opportunity to face up to these problems *in combination* — as they'll have to when the flight actually takes place. A training mock-up of the actual space capsule is being readied for the Astronauts, but even this will provide only control and navigation problems and will not be able to simulate stress or weightlessness.

This leaves only one place for the Astronauts to obtain a realistic simulation of orbital flight — in space. And that's the way they're going to do it — by taking a trial run into space before the orbital flight is attempted. In many respects, this training flight will be as dangerous as the orbit shot. Therefore, there must be detailed preparations, and an orderly progression of events preceding these practice flights. Here is the sequence of rocket firings that will take place before manned orbital flight is attempted:

(1) *Ballistic Firing of Empty Capsule.* The Mercury capsule will eventually be fired into orbit by an Atlas Booster— the largest operational rocket we now have available. But Atlas rockets are expensive (costing from $2 million to $30 million depending on how you figure it and whose estimate you accept) and aren't needed for all training flights. So some shots will be propelled by a special ballistic rocket booster consisting of a cluster of eight solid-propellent rockets and called "Little Joe," and others by a larger booster known as the Redstone (costing less than half as much as the Atlas) .

The first ballistic firing with a prototype of the Mercury capsule aboard took place on Sept. 9, 1959. The primary objective was to discover how the heat shield of the capsule would stand up under the heat and shock of re-entry into

A "Little Joe" rocket with a Mercury capsule aboard lifts off its launch pad at NASA's Wallops Station, Va., launch site. The "Little Joe" is used for low-powered Mercury tests.

the earth's atmosphere. Although the two outer booster engines failed to jettison, causing the capsule to fall some 200 miles from the scheduled impact spot, the tracking system operated well and the capsule was recovered speedily. Crews on recovery ships as far as 400 miles away saw the capsule flaming like a fireball when it re-entered the earth's atmosphere. The automatic parachutes opened as planned, and cushioned the descent of the capsule. The heat shield also passed its test with top marks. I examined the re-covered capsule — still draped with seaweed — in the NASA laboratories, and it appeared to be in perfect condition. There is little doubt that had a man been aboard, he would have survived the flight.

The Sept. 9 firing was the first of a series of such shots to be made with the empty capsule. Their purpose is to insure reliability of equipment — as far as possible — that the Astronauts will be using in their orbital flights. No one knows how many empty ballistic shots will be necessary, but the consensus at NASA headquarters is about a half-dozen — with the last few employing the actual Mercury capsule carrying full instrumentation.

(2) *Ballistic Firing of Capsule with Animals Aboard.* On Dec. 5, 1959, a seven-pound rhesus monkey named Sam was fished out of the North Atlantic by a United States destroyer. Sam was the first living creature to be sent aloft in a Mercury capsule. Strapped in a tiny form-fitting couch identical to those that the Astronauts will use, he was fired 55 miles into space by a Little Joe rocket. Sam's job was to test the escape mechanism mounted atop the Mercury capsule, and designed to bring the Astronaut inside safely back to earth if anything goes wrong.

Sam was blasted off from the NASA station at Wallops Island, Va. When the capsule reached an altitude of 20 miles, the escape rocket was automatically fired. Generating about 55,000 pounds of thrust, it lifted Sam's capsule away from the booster at a speed of 200 feet a second and propelled it to an altitude of 55 miles before the capsule lost its speed and began to descend. At 10,000 feet, a parachute opened automatically and eased the capsule into the Atlantic where it floated, awaiting rescue. The entire flight took 13 minutes.

A half-hour elapsed before a Navy Neptune bomber spotted the capsule, and it took another 45 minutes before the destroyer, *Brodie,* arrived on the scene. (Astronaut Alan Shepard, whose specialty is the recovery system, was aboard the destroyer.) When the capsule was lifted to the destroyer's deck and opened, Sam — still strapped securely in his cylindrical container inside — was hungry, frisky, and unmoved by his ride into space.

Test flights with animals aboard will be run off con-

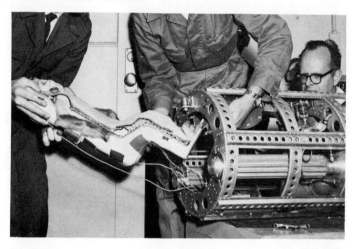

Preceding the Astronauts into space was this six-pound rhesus monkey named Miss Sam, pictured here shortly after she was retrieved from testing the capsule's escape mechanism.

currently with tests of the empty capsule. Again, there will probably be about a half-dozen such flights, each designed to test specific phases of the Mercury flight. The last few animal tests will duplicate the training rides to be taken by the Astronauts. The animals used will probably be monkeys or chimpanzees. The scientists would like to use a gorilla or a bear because their size and weight more nearly approximate those of a man, but these animals are extremely difficult to handle and can't be put under sedation without confusing the results of medical tests taken.

(3) *Ballistic Firing of Capsule with Man Aboard.* If we are to deal accurately with "firsts," the first American in space will actually be the first Astronaut to ride in a Redstone ballistic shot. Thus the orbital shot will — in a strictly dramatic sense — be anticlimactic. From a scientific viewpoint, however, the Redstone flights will produce only a

fraction of the information that will come out of the orbiting missions and are considered nothing more than training
flights.

The Redstone will carry the manned capsule about 100
miles into the air and some 175 miles out over the Atlantic
from Cape Canaveral; thus the trajectory will be pretty
much straight up and straight down. At the top of this trajectory, the Astronaut inside the capsule will have about
five minutes of weightlessness in which to find out how he
will react to the longer orbital flight to come.

The entire Redstone flight will take about 15 minutes,
and everything will be automatic. Stresses on the pilot will
not be as great as the orbital shot's, weightlessness will be
of shorter duration, acceleration less, and heating on re-
entry not as severe. But the five minutes of zero "G" will
be invaluable in preparing the pilots for the orbital shot.

The Redstone was selected as the booster for these training flights because it is less expensive, lower-powered, available, and reliable. Three or four — possibly more — of the
Astronauts will take the Redstone ride, with about a month
required between firings to get ready for the next one.
There is no schedule established, however, which has the
first man in the Redstone also being the first to attempt
orbital flight with the Atlas.

It's inevitable that great public emphasis will be placed
on "Who will be the first man to ride the Redstone into
space?" This is a dramatic question that makes for good
newspaper copy and certainly titillates the imagination of
the millions of people who have followed the evolution of
the Astronauts.

Yet, to those most closely involved — the Astronauts —
the question has much less significance. All of them will
undoubtedly go eventually, and all are qualified — so much
so that the first selection may be by lot. I personally doubt

A Redstone missile, backbone of the Project Mercury training program, awaits launching at Patrick Air Force Base, Fla. The Astronauts will take their first space ride on a Redstone.

this; I think it will be made on some less ethereal basis than chance. But however it's made, the scientific data gleaned by "the first man into space" of the Mercury program will be no more profound — and possibly less so — than that of those who will follow.

On this point, Gordon Cooper explained: "Even though drawing straws seems a haphazard way of choosing the first man up, think for a minute of the responsibility that will fall on the man who has to make the choice — if one is made. If all of us are qualified to take this ride — and I think we are — then why not avoid putting this responsibility on any individual by making the selection by lot?"

Although it's difficult for earthbound citizens to understand, each one of the Astronauts really does want to be the first man on both the Redstone and Atlas rides. As John Glenn told me emphatically: "Any guy who didn't really want to go first shouldn't be in this program."

By mid-1960, neither Russia nor the United States had successfully launched a man into space in a ballistic missile. American plans presently call for the first attempt to be made in the late fall of 1960, with the orbital flight following about a year later. American scientists insist the training flights are necessary to provide maximum safety to the Astronaut when he is finally launched into orbit. The Russians, however, might bypass these precautionary measures in an effort to get a man into orbit first. As mentioned earlier, there are rumors that they have already attempted the manned orbital flight and failed to recover the pilot.

One thing is certain: 1960 will be the year of decision for both nations in their man-into-space programs.

(4) *Orbital Flight and Recovery of the Empty Capsule.* The chances are about 50-50 that this step won't be judged necessary — particularly if the preceding steps have been satisfactorily carried out and the Atlas has proven its re-

The Astronauts may have to wait a long time for rescue. Here Wally Schirra relaxes in his life raft after climbing out of a boilerplate model of the Mercury capsule.

liability in other tests. The Atlas is expensive and in short supply, and if Mercury officials feel that no significant new data can be turned up by firing the empty capsule into orbit, they may very likely eliminate this step.

(5) *Orbital Flight with Animals.* The animals that prove best in the Redstone training flights will again be introduced to the Astronauts' couch — and this time sent into orbit. These flights will provide all the remaining necessary data for putting a man into orbit. Physiological reactions of the animals will be carefully observed, all of the automatic controls in the capsule will be checked in actual operation, and re-entry and recovery techniques will be tested.

Some of these five final steps in training may likely take place concurrently. For example, there may be orbital flights of animals while the Astronauts are still getting their space legs in the Redstone training flights.

The time between stages and the actual scheduling of each stage is impossible to predict. Probably no comparable scientific program in history has ever had more scheduling fluidity than Project Mercury. When officials say they don't know when the first space flight will be attempted, they're stating a simple and irrevocable fact. Why don't they know? Because the entire training program is accumulative. One stage can only follow the successful completion of the previous stage. Testing failures are costly, for we have neither the launching facilities nor the rockets to provide immediate back-up. This is one of the tragedies of our space program; the first team is excellent, but the second team simply doesn't exist. In a contest as crucial as this one, we should have reserves that can be moved immediately to the launching pad if one of the rockets fails to perform properly. This is a shortcoming that must be corrected before our man-into-space program can move ahead at top speed.

Another factor — hardly unexpected — that has complicated the Astronauts' training program is the constant demand from the press for interviews and information about them. This was mitigated somewhat by the decision of the Astronauts, a few weeks after the program was announced, to sell the first-person rights to their story exclusively to LIFE magazine — at a figure estimated from $100,000 to $500,000, to be divided equally among them. This contract was negotiated with the help of a Washington attorney named Leo DeOrsey, (who contributed his services to the young men without charge) after a bidding marathon between a half-dozen of the nation's largest magazines. As a result of this arrangement, most of the major magazines (except, of course, LIFE which has strenuously milked the story) have avoided feature articles on the Astronauts, giving the illusion that Mr. Luce is single-handedly sponsoring our man-into-space program.

Individual newspapers, the wire services, and radio and television networks have covered the Astronauts spasmodically; but under the terms of the LIFE contract, the Astronauts' homes and private lives are closed to reporters. Only one, a Canadian writer named Val Sears, penetrated this curtain. Before the defense forces were effectively marshaled, he tracked down several of the Astronauts in their homes. Since then, the young men have been affable and cooperative with reporters while on the job, but inaccessible at home.

This has had the effect of warding off many writers who might otherwise have stormed Langley Field — and led to the incongruous situation of the greatest news story in a decade getting most of its feature coverage from a single

The author lunches with Astronauts Slayton, Glenn, and Grissom in the Cafeteria at Project Mercury Headquarters, Langley Field, Va. Civilian employees pay little attention to the Astronauts.

magazine. An exception to this situation was POPULAR MECHANICS magazine which worked for six months in order to get me into Langley Field in October, 1959, to interview and photograph the Astronauts for a two-part magazine article. Col. John Powers, hard-bitten Air Force PIO who has been assigned to the Astronauts, shakes his head over this situation. "A few years back, reporters would have been using every trick in the business to get at these guys," he says. "Now they just sit in their offices and cry that they've been sold out."

The entire training program — from selection of the Astronauts to putting the first man in orbital flight — will take about two years. But the program won't end with the orbiting of the first Astronaut. Only the first phase will be over at that point. But the dramatic impact of that first orbital flight will be one of the most profound in the history of mankind.

Before we can discuss that flight intelligently, however, we need to know more about the "space hardware" — the vehicle in which the Astronaut will ride, the propellent force that will send him into space, and the labyrinth of scientific and mechanical equipment that will be required to return and recover him.

CHAPTER FIVE

SPACE HARDWARE

"There can be no respite in our drive, no flagging of effort. The tempo of our progress to date affords not the least grounds for complacency. . . , This is deadly serious business. We must put into it everything it takes."
—*Lt. Gen. Bernard A. Schriever, USAF*

For a half century, aircraft engineers and designers have been concerned with the concept of aircraft operating within the earth's atmosphere. Now a new frontier for manned flight has been opened: space. Since the problems of flight in space are quite different from those encountered in the earth's atmosphere, a new dimension of thinking must accompany the design and construction of space aircraft — or "space hardware" as the boys in the know call it. The fundamental differences are profound. For example:

Airplanes depend on the atmosphere for utilization of their motive power; rockets operate most efficiently in the vacuum of space;

Airplanes can make emergency landings in case of mechanical failure; space ships can't. There's no place to put down in space;

The space pilot can't bail out if he gets into trouble; he would simply follow the space ship in orbit;

Attitude changes in a space ship must be countered or they will continue indefinitely;

Distances and speeds in space are so great that even a minute error in control will magnify into a serious navigational problem.

Farsighted engineers and designers have been thinking about these — and many other — peculiarities of space flight for more than a decade, and they have most of the basic problems licked. But there are still hundreds of details that remain to be solved. It is with these details that the Astronauts and the Project Mercury scientists are now struggling.

Robert Gilruth, head of the Space Task Group that directs Project Mercury, says: "We don't need any new scientific breakthroughs to put a man into space and bring him back. We do, however, have a formidable engineering job ahead, and we expect many difficulties and surprises."

They're finding both. But day by day, one by one, the difficulties are being chipped away. Because space travel is a new frontier, the production of the "hardware" limits the speed at which the man-into-space program can move ahead. In an effort both to speed up the program and embody the pilots' ideas in the hardware, each of the Astronauts has been assigned a specific technical area in which to specialize. These are:

Carpenter: Navigation and navigational aids;
Cooper: Redstone booster;
Glenn: Crew space layout;
Grissom: Automatic and manual attitude-control system;
Schirra: Life support (atmospheric) system;
Shepard: Range, tracking, and recovery;
Slayton: Atlas booster.

SPACE HARDWARE

The Astronauts work closely with the manufacturers of equipment within their assigned areas — reporting back to the group as needed to keep each other abreast of current developments in every phase of the program.

Let's take a closer look, now, at the various elements of Project Mercury hardware to learn more about the mechanical equipment that will take the Astronauts into space.

(1) *Outside the Capsule*. The space ship which the Astronauts will pilot has — rather ingloriously — been labeled a capsule. Its dimensions were dictated by the size of the Atlas missile on which it will hitch a ride. Constructed of steel and shaped much like an oversized TV picture tube, the Mercury capsule is about 10 feet high and six feet in diameter at its broadest point. Its basic components include a parachute housing, antenna cannister, pilot's pressurized compartment, heat shield, and escape system.

Some remarkable things are demanded of the Mercury capsule. It must be capable of withstanding the stresses of acceleration from zero to 18,000 m.p.h. and then back to zero again. It must be aerodynamically stable to permit absolute directional accuracy during firing and re-entry. It must withstand friction heat up to 2,000° F. when it re-enters the earth's atmosphere — and protect its passenger from this killing temperature. It must be strong enough to withstand severe loading and heating without deforming so much that it loses its trajectory.

Of these problems, proper protection of the human passenger against the extreme heat of re-entry was the most difficult to solve. It was breached — as most such profound problems seem to be — by a simple discovery made by an NASA scientist named H. Julian Allen. For years scientists had used sleek, streamlined shapes for experiments with space vehicles. Although useful in other ways, they offered

Before full-size capsules were fired into space, hundreds of tests were conducted with scale models like this one being observed in a vertical wind tunnel at Langley Research Center.

little protection against excessive heat. When a streamlined hypersonic missile re-entered the earth's atmosphere, it simply burned up.

Five years ago, Allen came up with the concept of using a blunt, snubbed-nose shape that throws some 99 percent of the heat ahead into the atmosphere in the form of shock waves which form a shield of air in front of the missile and keep it from burning up. This knowledge was first made public in a dramatic television demonstration by President Eisenhower in May, 1957. He fondled the first missile nose cone we had been able to recover from outer space and explained the import of this experiment to millions of Americans. It is doubtful if many of them understood its significance.

From this discovery evolved the heat shield now attached to the blunt end of the Mercury capsule. There have been

The Astronauts, who have had a hand in designing their own space equipment, appear cheerful as they examine an early full-size model of the capsule they will ride into space.

A model of the Mercury capsule is positioned in the huge wind tunnel at Langley Field preparatory to testing it for lift, drag, and static stability characteristics.

several tests of this heat shield that have proven its ability to protect a human occupant inside. The margin of error, however, is slight. Because the shield covers only the forward portion of the capsule, it is essential that the space vehicle hit the atmosphere at precisely the right angle to insure maximum protection. An error of a few degrees in either direction would expose the capsule skin directly to temperatures that would parboil anything alive inside the capsule. Scott Carpenter pointed out to me, however, that the capsule is aerodynamically designed in such a way that it *has to* maintain the proper angle when it hits the earth's atmosphere — even if controls are ineffectual.

The parachute housing is in the narrow top portion of the capsule. It contains three parachutes: a small drogue chute to open at 42,000 feet, a larger chute that will open at 10,000 feet and lower the capsule to the water at

MERCURY CAPSULE

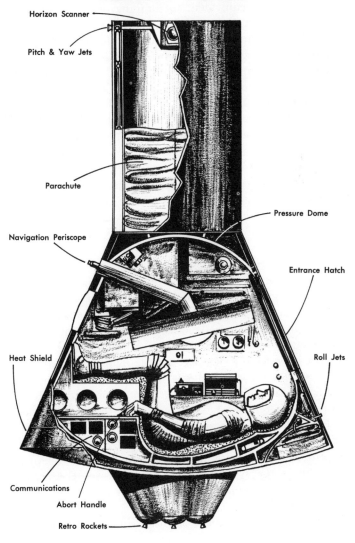

Horizon Scanner

Pitch & Yaw Jets

Parachute

Navigation Periscope

Pressure Dome

Entrance Hatch

Heat Shield

Roll Jets

Communications

Abort Handle

Retro Rockets

a speed of about 30 feet per second (producing a ground impact roughly equivalent to jumping off a 15-foot wall), and a reserve chute for safety.

The latest innovation for the capsule is an enormous rubberized fiberglass cushion which is folded behind the heat shield during most of the flight. When the large parachute has slowed the capsule's descent to its minimum speed, the heat shield will be uncoupled by the Astronaut. As it falls away, it will bring down a four-foot-high skirt designed to provide a cushion of air between the capsule and the ground or water.

The escape system — supported on a structural framework about 10 feet high — is mounted atop the narrow end of the capsule and contains its own rocket propellent system. Its purpose is to propel the capsule with its human occupant off the top of the Atlas booster in the event that anything goes wrong with the mission between the launching and orbiting of the capsule.

The escape system will be activated automatically in case of an emergency abort (for example, if the Atlas were to explode on the launching pad). It can also be activated by the pilot in the capsule or by central control at Cape Canaveral. Thus if the pilot is unable to act, he can still be cut loose from a defective missile by ground control.

When the abort handle is pulled (engineers call it a "chicken switch" — a term the pilots find extremely distasteful), it releases a series of clamps that hold the capsule to the Atlas booster. Then, an escape rocket fires, lifting the capsule off and away from the Atlas. When the capsule reaches maximum altitude, the framework supporting the escape system is blown away from the capsule, automatically opening a parachute that lowers the capsule to the ground.

(2) *Inside the Capsule.* Another simple scientific break-

through was required to make space travel possible for man. The tremendous stresses to which the space pilot is subjected during launch and re-entry had always been a major problem. These stresses could be lethal. Eight times his weight (eight "G's") was the maximum force a seated pilot could take and still control his craft — and stresses for space flight would exceed eight "G's". What to do?

The answer was ludicrously simple. Put the pilot in a reclining position. Tests quickly showed that man could control his vehicle at much greater "G"-loads in a supine — instead of a sitting — position.

So the space pilot was put on a couch, with his knees slightly above his head. As a result, the interior of the Mercury capsule had to be designed around the pilot's couch which stretches across the entire bottom of the vehicle. (The height of the Astronauts was limited to a

This antiseptic, dust-free production line has been created at the Mc-Donnell Aircraft Corporation plant in St. Louis to turn out Project Mercury space capsules.

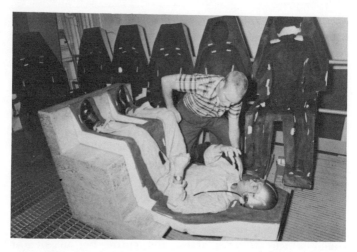

Each pilot's couch is molded to fit his bodily contours. Here Astronaut Alan Shepard makes a mold from which his space-capsule couch will be patterned.

One discovery that helped make manned space flight possible is the contour couch—by reclining in it, an Astronaut can withstand the stresses of going into and returning from space.

maximum of 5 feet 11 inches by the diameter of the capsule.) Each of the seven Astronauts has been fitted to his own individually-molded couch.

Placement of the controls and instrument panel in the capsule had to be carefully considered. During moments of high stress, the pilot will be unable to move his head and must thus be able to see everything he needs to see simply by moving his eyes. There are three elements fully visible to him by eye movement alone; the instrument panel, the periscope giving him a view of the earth below, and a window looking out on the heavens above.

The instrument panel is set directly at eye level. The periscope eyepiece — an eight-inch lens — is two feet from the pilot's face and slightly below eye level. At orbiting altitude, the pilot will be able to see a vista of 1,700 miles of the earth's surface through the periscope. It will normally be trained on the earth, but by changing the attitude of the space ship the pilot can see in any direction. The window is located slightly above the pilot's eye level and will give him a view of the horizon when the periscope is aimed at the earth.

The peculiarities of space flight require a single hand control easily accessible to the Astronaut, who will be under extreme stress during launch and re-entry and weightless in orbit — both difficult conditions under which to make coordinated hand movements. The control, located at the pilot's right hand, combines in one handle the three attitude corrections the Astronaut will have to make: pitch, roll, and yaw.

A forward-and-back motion opens hydrogen peroxide jets on the outside of the capsule which correct pitch (a tumbling movement); a sideways motion corrects roll; and a twisting motion controls yaw (movement about the vertical axis).

Although design of the cockpit was one of the first steps completed in the Mercury program, it also spawned a considerable argument among the Astronauts that still hasn't been resolved to their entire satisfaction. Because the three-dimensional control sometimes gives the pilot a yaw movement when he doesn't call for it, several of the Astronauts — led by Wally Schirra — wanted the yaw control operated by foot pedals, leaving only two movements on the hand control. They lost the argument, partly on the grounds that no one knew whether sufficient foot movement would be possible in the capsule. This, of course, can be modified after the manned capsule has been tested in space.

The capsule is also equipped with an automatic pilot which calls for immediate corrections by means of hydrogen jets when the capsule deviates from its intended attitude. The automatic pilot is not yet foolproof; it occasionally picks up stray signals which confuse the mechanism, and the outside jets have been slow in reacting to controls — both manual and automatic. It is these kinds of technical problems that persist in popping up, and which must be solved before the first manned flight.

A constant atmosphere (equivalent to that at 27,000 feet) is maintained on the inside of the capsule — much like the cabin pressure on commercial airliners. An air-conditioning unit cools the capsule during periods of excessive heat, and de-humidifiers remove the moisture caused by pilot perspiration. Filter traps are thoughtfully provided to prevent any solid objects — floating about during the weightless period of orbit — from colliding with any of the vital organs of the capsule.

The Astronaut will enter the capsule through a hatch in its side which is then sealed from the inside. He may get out by blowing off this hatch (thus causing the capsule

This is the instrument panel in the centrifuge. The space capsule panel will be similar, with all the buttons and switches within easy reach of the prone Astronaut.

to sink if it is resting on water) or by removing a portion of the instrument panel and climbing out the top of the capsule. This latter route is recommended unless an emergency requires him to get out quickly — a situation which Project Mercury officials are going to extreme pains to avoid.

(3) *Booster Power.* The Astronauts will be blasted into space by America's most powerful operational missile, the Atlas, made in San Diego by the Convair Division of the General Dynamics Corporation. The Atlas is the free world's first extensively-tested intercontinental ballistic missile (ICBM), and also the first complete missile to achieve an earth-circling orbit. The Atlas will provide the muscle for most of our early space explorations.

Convair began studies on the space capabilities of the Atlas in 1952. When the United States finally awakened to

With an explosive roar, the Atlas thunders off the launch pad at Cape Canaveral. The Astronauts will ride atop a similar rocket, and be blasted into space by its 360,000-pound thrust.

the dawning of the Space Age after Sputnik I, Convair had the Atlas program ready to go. A year later (in December, 1958), an Atlas missile was launched into orbit carrying a tape-recorded message from President Eisenhower.

The first words broadcast from space were: "This is the President of the United States speaking. Through the marvels of scientific advance, my voice is coming to you from a satellite circling in outer space. My message is a simple one. Through this unique means I convey to you and to all mankind America's wish for peace on earth and good will toward men everywhere."

The Atlas is a liquid-fuel rocket with more than enough power (350,000 pounds thrust) to put the Mercury capsule into orbit. Without the Mercury capsule, the Atlas stands 82 feet high and weighs 260,000 pounds. Its diameter is 10 feet.

A worm's eye view of the Atlas propulsion system shows the twin-chambered booster at left and right, and sustainer in the middle. These engines have hurled an Atlas more than 9,000 miles.

This long line of stainless steel Atlas missiles is part of the production line at the San Diego plant of the Convair Division of General Dynamic Corporation. They're for both military and space use.

Early in 1960, Deke Slayton, whose specialty is the Atlas, told me: "There's no question about the ability of the Atlas to put us into orbit; our only problem here is reliability which so far isn't good enough. But we know it will be by the time we're ready to use it."

The Astronauts will use the Atlas only for their orbital flights. The practice rides on the missile range will be taken in the Redstone booster. Redstone missiles are produced for the U.S. Army at Huntsville, Ala. The motors — also powered by liquid fuel — come from North American Aviation in Southern California. An Astronaut can ride in the capsule mounted on the Redstone for a maximum distance of 175 miles.

Project Mercury scientists have also developed a special booster for the man-into-space program. A cluster of eight solid-propellant rockets, it's known as Little Joe — because it's so much smaller (and cheaper), than other rockets in the program. Little Joe is used to launch capsule test vehicles and to test the capsule escape mechanism.

(4) *Pressure Suits.* Less than 30 years ago, Wiley Post made a deadstick landing after an engine failure over the Mojave Desert. Clambering laboriously from the cockpit of his plane, Post waddled toward a car approaching him on a nearby highway. The motorist took one startled look at Post and gunned his car desperately to get away. He could scarcely be blamed. Post was testing one of the early aircraft pressure suits, and to the frightened motorist, he must have looked the part of a newly-arrived Martian.

Things have changed. Space suits are not yet equated with everyday street attire, but they're no longer uncommon to pilots and small boys who want someday to become pilots. The Astronauts will wear the most advanced space suits yet created — and they'll be needed.

There is no point within our solar system (except earth)

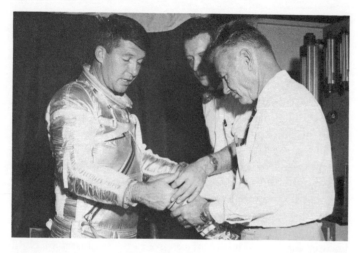

Wally Schirra, the Astronauts' specialist in space haberdashery, here has a fitting of the new space suit which has been specially designed for Project Mercury by the Goodrich Tire and Rubber Company.

which offers an environment hospitable to man. Thus, if he ventures into space, man must take a life-sustaining environment with him. This is the function of the space suit.

In its most important sense, though, the space suit is a safety valve. It will permit the Astronaut a living atmosphere in case anything goes wrong with the atmospheric pressure created in the capsule. If the cabin system fails, the Astronaut can isolate himself in his pressure suit.

The pressure suit to be worn by the Astronauts consists of two layers. The outer suit — a single layer of reinforced rubber — will be pressurized only if the capsule pressure fails. But beneath the outer suit, the orbiting Astronaut will wear an inner garment to provide space between the outer garment and his body; through this, ventilating air will be passed. Air will flow into the inner suit through a

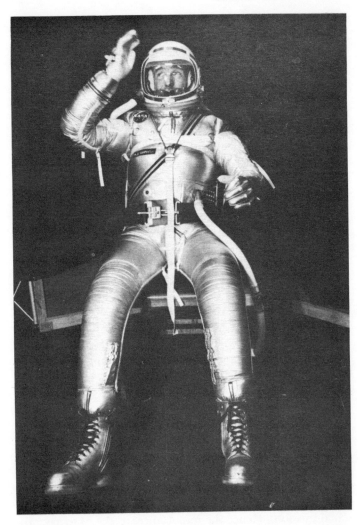

If necessary, the Astronaut can create his own atmosphere inside his space suit. Here, Scott Carpenter moves his arms to test mobility in one of the development models of the Mercury pressure suit.

waist connection, circulate through the suit, and be exhausted through a pipe in the helmet. The air will then move through an air-conditioning system under the Astronaut's couch, where impurities will be purged before recirculation. The Astronaut will have to live with any body odors that are picked up when the air is circulated through his pressure suit, even though they will be purged each time around. One really serious difficulty the orbiting Astronaut might face is the passing of gas while he's in the pressure suit. He can't escape the odor and it might be overpowering. For this and other reasons he'll be fed a special diet for five days before the flight.

In orbit the temperature in the capsule will be in the 70's, and if the cabin environmental system is working properly, the Astronaut will be able to open the face plate of his pressure suit. During launch and re-entry the extreme heat on the outside of the capsule will raise the cabin temperature to as high as 150°; but the Astronaut won't feel this in his ventilated pressure suit.

The suits are coated with a silver spray which acts as an additional heat buffer and radioactive shield. The helmet also protects the Astronaut from the deafening noise of the rocket engines during the launching period. The seven Astronauts eventually will have a wardrobe of 20 pressure suits — at a cost of about $3,800 each.

(5) *Communications and Navigation.* Manned space flight is of limited value unless the wealth of information it turns up is transmitted effectively and accurately to the ground. Some of this information can be reported by the pilot when he returns from a successful space flight. But a great deal more can come from the capsule during the actual mission. Hence the importance, to the Mercury program, of an effective communications system.

The Astronaut will communicate with earthbound humans in two significant ways. One is involuntary. Sensitive electrodes attached to the body of the Astronaut will send constant detailed information on body temperature, pulse, and respiration to a series of receiving stations which will record and convert the telemetered data almost instantaneously to understandable data. This, in turn, will be relayed within seconds to a battery of medical specialists charged with the physical well-being of the Astronaut. If the Astronaut falters physically during the flight, the medics will know almost immediately and will order the capsule returned to earth.

The Astronaut will also have normal voice communication with the ground. Earphones and a microphone are mounted inside the headpiece of the pressure suit. Radio transmission in space is excellent; there are no local noises with which to contend. The only difficulty — and one which regularly plagues missile scientists — is the possible jamming of radio frequencies. Most of the trouble comes from Latin American "ham" radio operators. Although unintentional, the jamming causes frequent lapses in the radio communication with space probes.

Both navigation and communications will be dependent on a series of tracking stations placed strategically around the world. (One of Russia's main difficulties in its man-into-space program is in establishing a world-wide system of tracking stations; the USSR doesn't always have friends in the right places.) The location of the 14 American tracking stations is now established, but funds were still lacking in mid-1960 to build all the necessary facilities on the tracking sites.

According to Scott Carpenter — in whose specialty it falls — navigation is a misnomer when applied to space flight.

"Once the capsule is separated from the booster or in orbit, you're committed to your course," he says. "There's

Microphones have been built into the facepiece of the space suit. Scott Carpenter, communications specialist, tests his voice system before taking a training flight.

no correction except downward."

Even though he can't alter his course, the Astronaut will be able to track himself by visual reference to the ground — where he will have a 190-degree field of vision encompassing 1,700 miles of the earth's surface.

It's essential that the orbiting Astronaut know where he is at all times because he will have to activate the re-entry rockets if the automatic system should fail — and this poses a delicate problem in navigation. The tiniest error in the time or location of starting the re-entry cycle changes the recovery point by many miles (an error of one second causes an error of five miles in landing location). And the closer the capsule comes to the spot in the North Atlantic where the rescue fleet is waiting, the better the chance of its recovery. The Atlantic is a large ocean, and the capsule a minute piece of flotsam — even when it's the object of what will probably be history's most thorough searching team.

It is also important to the well-being of the capsule pilot that he bring his vehicle down on water. Although he would probably survive a land drop, the impact would be much greater than on water.

(6) *The X-15 and Dyna-Soar.* There is vast public confusion as to the part played in the man-into-space program by the X-15 airplane (and its well-publicized pilot, Scott Crossfield) and the more recent Air Force experimental aircraft euphemistically named Dyna-Soar. *Neither of these vehicles has any direct connection with Project Mercury.* But because they are often grouped in the public mind with the Mercury program, let's examine them briefly and put them in perspective in relation to Project Mercury.

The X-15 grew out of an NASA study which, in 1954, specified performance figures for a research airplane to explore hypersonic speeds and space flight. The project was turned over to the Air Force which invited bids in December, 1954; six months later, the job of building three such aircraft was awarded to North American Aviation.

Thus, the X-15 has been on the drawing board, in construction, and under test since late in 1955. The X-15 made its first powered flight on Sept. 17, 1959, but by May of 1960 had still not successfully penetrated space.

The X-15 has a 400,000-horsepower engine that can be throttled and is capable of being shut down and re-started in flight. It uses 10,000 pounds of fuel per minute — some 20 times as much as a modern jet aircraft with afterburners. Most of the engine controls, indicators, and instruments are similar to those in a conventional aircraft, with the addition of a second set of controls to correct pitch, roll, and yaw in space flight.

The X-15 will attempt space flight on an instrumented

Here is the X-15 at its moment of launch. It has just been dropped from the wing of its mother ship and will soon blast spaceward under its own rocket power.

flight range extending from Wendover, Utah, to Edwards Air Force Base in Southern California. On its test flights, it will be launched at 38,000 feet from under the wing of a B-52 bomber. A propellent rocket will fire the X-15 into a ballistic trajectory that will peak at about 100 miles altitude. (Project Mercury calls for an orbit at 120 miles.) When the rocket fuel burns out (about three minutes after launch), the X-15 will coast silently in a weightless arc for about six minutes, then descend into the earth's atmosphere. During the re-entry period, the pilot will have to exercise precise control to prevent the airplane from disintegrating or burning in the tremendous heat and loading that will be experienced. In time spent in outer space, the X-15 test flights will be roughly comparable to the Astronauts' training rides atop the Redstone booster.

As the X-15 test pilot, Scott Crossfield's obligation (and

that of his employer, North American Aviation) is simply to fly three times the speed of sound at an altitude of 150,-000 feet. Once this mission has been successfully accomplished, the X-15 will be turned over to NASA and the Air Force — which have much more ambitious plans for it. Air Force test pilots, led by Capt. Robert White, eventually hope to push the X-15 to altitudes of 400 miles or more above the earth. But this is still several years away. The X-15 test-pilot pool will include specially trained NASA, Air Force, and Naval aviators who will gradually increase the X-15's performance until it reaches its maximum capacity in space.

The Dyna-Soar is a much more ambitious project than the X-15. Where Crossfield will be poking about on the fringes of space, Dyna-Soar will take the full plunge.

In November, 1959, the Air Force announced that the

Standing beside the X-15 are the three men charged with putting it through its paces: from left to right, pilots Joseph Walker (NASA), Robert White (USAF), and Scott Crossfield (North American Aviation).

Boeing Airplane Company would manufacture the Dyna-Soar vehicle; the rocket booster to put it into space will be produced by the Martin Company. A small group of Air Force pilots is already in preliminary training to handle the Dyna-Soar and other USAF space ships.

The Dyna-Soar (a contraction of "dynamic soaring") has a specific mission in addition to space exploration: it will also be capable of such military missions as reconnaissance and possibly bombing, if the latter proves practicable. Like the Mercury capsule, the Dyna-Soar will be launched from the ground and boosted into space by a powerful rocket — probably a Titan. The rocket will drop away at an altitude of 100 miles, and Dyna-Soar's 75,000-pound thrust engine will cut in to hurl the space ship into its chosen trajectory orbiting around the earth. Re-entry will be controlled by the pilot; he will accomplish it by dipping into the earth's atmosphere, then quickly getting out to avoid too severe heating of the aircraft. His descent will be a deliberate series of such dips, until the plane can be controlled aerodynamically to a normal landing.

Here, briefly, are the major points of difference between the three American man-into-space programs:

Dyna-Soar is strictly military; Project Mercury is strictly civilian; the X-15 is a combination of both.

Dyna-Soar and the X-15 are winged-glide vehicles; Mercury is a capsule.

Pilots of the Dyna-Soar and X-15 will be able to control their aircraft to a landing; the Mercury pilot will not be able to exert aerodynamic control.

Mercury and Dyna-Soar will be launched by ground rockets; the X-15 will be launched from another aircraft.

Mercury and Dyna-Soar will attain orbital flight; the X-15 won't.

Mercury and the X-15 will make brief excursions into

space sometime in 1960, but Dyna-Soar won't follow until four or five years later. Project Mercury will be years ahead of any other American program for putting a man into orbit around the earth.

* * *

This, then, is the hardware which the Astronauts and their fellow travelers in space will be using. It's a highly volatile field in which profound changes can be expected as we broaden our knowledge through actual excursions into space.

But the first explorations will be made with the hardware just described. The most dramatic flight — and certainly the most important as far as international prestige is concerned — will be the first orbital shot of the Mercury capsule sometime in 1961. This is the moment toward which all of Project Mercury's efforts are being mustered — a moment that will be watched with equal curiosity and awe by Chinese peasants, Ghana bus drivers, German industrialists, Czech storekeepers, Russian bureaucrats, and let us hope, American citizens.

So let's go along with the first Astronaut as he's fired into orbit. I asked the Astronauts to project for me, in detail, the events and excitement of this first orbital shot. Following is an account of this historic trip as the men who will experience it described it to me.

CHAPTER SIX

FLIGHT INTO SPACE

> "No instrument or array of instruments exists
> that can duplicate the sensing capabilities of a
> man. When to this is added man's capability to
> record, remember, interpret, and discriminate,
> we see how paltry are the powers of the most
> sophisticated mechanical substitute."
>
> —*M. W. Rosen and F. C. Schwenk,*
> *NASA scientists*

This is Cape Canaveral. The month is September. The year, 1961.

A repressed air of excitement hovers over this place where excitement is an everyday occurrence. There's a different smell, a different feel. No one articulates it. It's just there — unwritten, unspoken, unidentifiable — but there.

Perhaps it's because the Mercury Astronauts have been at Cape Canaveral for more than a week. This has never happened before — even during the Redstone tests. There's been no effort to hide their presence. But no explanation, either. It's been almost a year, now, since the first Astronaut took a training flight atop the Redstone booster. Perhaps the time has finally come . . . It would be welcome news in a world where the United States is struggling desperately to re-assert itself.

It's hot in Florida. Even at Canaveral, perched on the point of a triangle poking into the Atlantic, halfway down the Florida east coast, the ocean breezes are fetid and lackluster. The palmettos and scrub — only native inhabitants remaining on this bleak bit of sandy real estate — barely stir, day or night. All of this unseasonable stillness adds to the breathless air of expectancy about the place.

The Astronauts neither contribute to it nor undermine it. They wander about the Cape in twos or threes, asking questions, exploring facilities, discussing technical problems. Only the Astronauts — and a half-dozen of their superiors — have any knowledge of the drama that took place in the office of the director of Project Mercury 10 days earlier.

He had addressed himself with unusual solemnity to the pilots who had been training — under his direction — for two years for the first manned orbital flight around the earth.

"The time has come," he told them. "We're as ready as we can ever expect to be. We can never eliminate all the risks, but I think we've done everything humanly possible to guarantee reliability and safety in the equipment you men are going to use. Now we're ready to turn the job over to you."

The Astronauts had listened calmly. They'd been psychologically prepared for this moment many months ago. The waiting since then had been vexing and restless. They were overtrained and eager. The announcement was more a relief than anything else to them.

"One of you will be fired into orbit in 10 days," the director continued. "The rest of you will get a chance at the same ride later. This isn't a one-man job. It's a team effort. You all know that. But the fact remains that only one man can go at a time — and someone has to go first.

You men are all well qualified, and we gave serious thought to pulling the name out of a hat. It was a tough decision for any man or group of men to make. But we talked it over and took a vote; and we discovered that a majority agreed on one of you as having just a shade of advantage for this first ride. Maybe the next one will be chosen by lot. But those of us in charge of the program are willing to take the responsibility for naming the first Mercury pilot."

He paused, not consciously exploiting the theatrics of the moment but genuinely concerned at the import of his message. Then he looked searchingly at the seven men before him — and named a name.

There were a few seconds of absolute silence — then a subdued sort of pandemonium. The man he had named sat dazedly in his chair; the others surrounded him, pummeling and congratulating him. The lifting of tension was acute. The relief could almost be seen and touched. The early spirit of Project Mercury that had sagged and faltered during the last months of waiting was magically revived. The show — at long last — was on the road!

* * *

It is early morning — very early morning — at Cape Canaveral. A large ground crew has been working all night in the brilliance of floodlights. They were joined at midnight by another group, routed from bed. Whenever this happens, the workmen know that something alive — or someone — is going up in the capsule. When the booster is blasted off well before dawn, the rescue fleet will have a maximum number of daylight hours to search for the returned capsule in the waters of the Atlantic — before darkness pulls a shade on the rescue operations.

This early morning at Cape Canaveral is luminescent, even in corners where the floodlights don't reach. A three-quarter moon looks down bemusedly — and, to some, invitingly — on the scene of bustling activity. The Atlas stands out stark and black against the sandy flatness, and the gantry about it resembles an incredibly complex spider web.

The Atlas has been fueled, and the trucks are withdrawing from the firing area. Workers — some still rubbing sleep from their eyes — find themselves moving with an inexplicable sense of urgency. They are clearing away the fueling paraphernalia when a small group of men emerge from the blockhouse and approach the gantry. They talk briefly at the bottom, then slowly begin to ascend toward the capsule resting atop the Atlas.

For a moment, activity around the gantry ceases. Busy hands hesitate, graven, in mid-air. Steps freeze. There's an almost audible drawing of breath from dozens of throats. For, in the midst of that group of men, one stands out sharply. He's clad in a pressure suit, and one of the other members of the group is carrying his helmet. As the men start to climb the gantry, the tempo of work below ignites with a spark of exhilaration. *This* is the day.

* * *

He's been immobile in the capsule for almost an hour, now. There was no way to avoid that agonizing hour's wait — reclining above an unexploded bomb that would soon be armed and detonated; it takes an hour to clear the firing area, and he had to be in the capsule before the gantry was moved away. But there was incessant chatter, and the checking of instruments to occupy him, and for this he's grateful.

Now the hour is almost up. The countdown has reached . . .

"Zero minus five."

"God bless you," he hears unexpectedly on his headset,

and he knows the Astronaut on the radio at the blockhouse speaks for the anxious people sweating out this moment at Cape Canaveral — and millions of others who will learn about it over their breakfast coffee later in the morning...

"We interrupt this program to announce that the United States has successfully put a man into orbit..."

In a warm wave of gratitude he reflects for an instant how satisfying it is to have four of the Astronauts to talk with at the control center. They understand what's going on in the capsule — and in his thoughts — without needless explanation. Soon — if all goes well — he'll hear the other two: one at the tracking station in Australia, the other with the rescue fleet that will salvage him from the Atlantic in about three and one-half hours.

"Zero minus three."

He realizes a little reproachfully that his colleagues kept him so busy on the radio he hadn't spent any of the last hour thinking about God. He does so now. His lips move inside the face window of his space suit.

"Zero minus two . . ."

"Zero minus one."

Eternity stands suspended.

Then all the thunderclaps in history reunite for a brief instant beneath him.

His body strains.

His ears throb.

But his thoughts remain clear and concise, focused on the instrument panel before him, searching for warnings of trouble.

Then he hears a shout of sheer delight and exuberance in his headset, and he knows the launching has been successful.

The exhilaration of taking a new aircraft aloft, of breaking bonds with earthbound humans rolls over him in great

The bird is away! The Atlas—trailing three massive jets of flame—pushes into the darkness of outer space, carrying its Astronaut passenger to man's most exciting adventure.

joyous waves, and he knows an excitement so intense it seems he can no longer contain it. But mixed with the excitement is a growing, pounding feeling of immense pressure.

The moment of firing had been almost deafening. The sound exploded through the walls of the capsule and through his helmet with a shattering that sent sharp arrows of pain darting about his head for an instant before subsiding. Except for the sound, the sensations of launching were almost nonexistent.

Now, a minute from the launching pad, the pressure grows steadily as the Atlas finds less resistance in the atmosphere to the thrust of its powerful engines. The weight of a hundred mountains slowly begins to engulf him and push him down and down into the couch until it seems he must come out the other side. For the first time in the past two years, he fully appreciates those punishing hours in the centrifuge that conditioned him for this experience. Although the pressure seems greater than he remembers it in the centrifuge, he feels no fear. He watches his instruments carefully; the clock, set to start at the instant of launch, shows that he was fired from the pad just two-and-a-half minutes ago.

He raises his gloved hand with an effort and touches the abort switch. A twist and a pull on this handle, and a rocket over his head would wrench him loose from the Atlas and a parachute would drop him, not gently, back to earth. There's no temptation to pull the switch. None at all.

Just two minutes, he thinks, *and I'll never have to use this.*

His head feels as if it were being squeezed between the palms of an omnipotent giant. His vision fuzzes, then comes clear again as he exerts a conscious effort to concentrate on his instruments. The throbbing reverberation of the blast has finally dissipated, but in its place is a persistent ringing that annoys him. All of these things he's experienced before; only the degree is different. It borders now on the intolerable.

The clock says three-and-one-half minutes from launch.

In his headset he hears: "The launch was perfect. The bird is exactly on trajectory. You will go into orbit in 40 seconds. Are you okay?"

He says thickly, "Okay, okay," into the microphone in his helmet.

His eyes are fastened on the clock. Forty seconds. An eternity of seconds. All he sees now is the clock. The edge of consciousness closes in around him, tighter and tighter, until the only fragmentary unit of conscious thought left him is the tiny face of the clock. Twenty seconds. Fifteen Ten. Five.

Then he reaches the top of the roller coaster. The long, grueling climb is over. Wonderfully, he mounts the crest and the whole world spreads out below him in a panorama of delicious clarity. His stomach comes loose for an instant from the rest of him, then settles uneasily back in place. The pressure relaxes, then disappears — replaced by a feeling of near-ethereality, as if he doesn't really exist in a body at all. The thought occurs to him that perhaps he has just died; then another less clear, but more disturbing thought: that perhaps we don't really die at all, that this is how it feels, and he is being given a preview — the first man to be so privileged . . . But he brushes the thought aside. There are other things to do now.

Above him, he knows the escape tower has fallen away — no longer needed. *That* moment of crisis, at least, has passed. Below him, the vehicle that carried him into space — the Atlas — has also fallen away, its job completed. Only the Mercury capsule remains — a man-made stone cast free into the heavens by the mind and muscle of science.

* * *

In the blockhouse at Cape Canaveral — a drab concrete building stuffed with expensive and ingenious electronic equipment — several dozen men hover around two men: the range safety officer and the communications officer. Most of them are in sport shirts, already wet with perspiration, although the Florida sun is just beginning to find an exploratory handhold on the eastern horizon.

Excitement permeates every corner of the room. Eyes are bright, mouths half open in a state of suspended wonderment. There seems to be a subconscious feeling that if anyone expresses his joy aloud, the accomplishment may somehow still be negated. So only the communications officer speaks, although the room is full of repressed sound.

As the Atlas is launched, the technicians at Cape Canaveral's Central Control are tense and fearful, watching the telemetering machines— like in the ninth inning of a no-hit game.

He says: "Are you reading me in the capsule? Are you okay? Do you have control of the ship?"

For a few seconds, there is no breath in any of the men in the blockhouse. The telemetering machine clicks inexorably away, transmitting from space to earth the heartbeat and the respiration of the man in the capsule.

Then he speaks.

His voice is faint, but clear and incisive.

"I'm okay. I have control of the ship." A pause, then: "My God — what an experience."

The way he says it, it sounds more like a prayer than a curse.

* * *

The capsule must be turned, and he tries to ignore the excitement building in him as he goes about this prosaic piece of business.

Five minutes later, with the capsule in a perfect orbit and the Astronaut safe, the tension subsides and they all breathe again. This is the moment towards which they have all been working.

Cautiously and slowly, he raises his right hand to grasp the control lever. His whole body rises against the restraining straps on the couch, and his hand continues an upward arc until it, too, is restrained. Then he starts a slow, tortuous descent of his arm to the control handle. His hand hits it with a thump that tingles the palm inside his glove. His fingers close over the handle.

A slight forward pressure opens hydrogen peroxide jets outside the capsule. As he watches the periscope screen, the earth comes clearly into view. Back pressure on the control, and the rotation stops. Spread out below him is the vastness of the Atlantic. But more than that. He can see clearly the islands of the West Indies; and *he can also see the western coast of Africa.* The immensity of this strikes him so sharply that he's almost unaware of two other phenomena. He's in bright sunlight; and there is no sound.

This photograph, taken from an Atlas, gives an idea of what the first Astronaut to orbit the earth will see. Africa is visible at left and South America on the horizon.

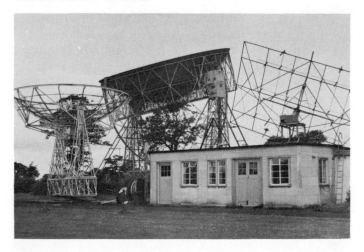

All around the world, tracking stations like this one turn a sensitive ear to outer space to record the flight of the Astronaut as he streaks about the earth at 17,400 m.p.h.

Not a whisper of sound. Not even his radio. Nothing.

He's surprised to discover that in this vastness of the universe, looking on the heavens as they've never been seen before by earthmen, he feels himself more important, more significant than ever before in his life. He sees with a sharp wave of insight his own position in the universe: that without him, somehow, it wouldn't be complete — just as it would be incomplete without any of the men anxiously awaiting his return to earth. The pieces of the universe fit together for him as they never have before, and he feels a strange — but oddly comfortable — mixture of humility and self-satisfaction. Raising his eyes, he sees a skyful of unblinking polka-dots of red, white, and blue — the stars of the universe, with the fog of earth's atmosphere dropped magically away from them. They are clearly visible in the bright sunlight, with the sun at his back and out of sight.

This instant of silence, of wonderment, of realization, and fulfillment is brief. There is a voice in his earphones now, saying:

"Are you reading me in the Mercury capsule? This is the Canary tracking station. If you read me, please acknowledge."

"You're coming in loud and clear," he hears himself saying.

There's no mistaking the excitement in the voice from the Canary Islands.

"How are you? What's going on up there? Give us a report if you can."

This is the way it will be all the way around, he reflects. Each new tracking station — 14 of them — passing him from one to the next, all wanting to know the same things: how is he and what is he seeing? How can he put the excitement and exhilaration into words — ever. He can only hint, in totally inadequate language, of the new frontiers that have been opened to man this day.

Back at central control, the tension has eased a bit. The same men are hovering over the same radar-scopes and telemetering machines, but now they're more relaxed. Talk is still hushed, as if — in the ninth inning of a no-hitter — it's best not to talk straight out until the deed is done and completed. The grounded Astronauts are grouped about the telemeter, watching it click out a steady drone of information being gathered from other tracking stations around the world. Several doctors are examining this data with no effort to conceal their elation.

"How is he, doc?" asks one of the Astronauts, already knowing the answer but still seeking assurance.

"Perfect," is the answer. "Perfect, by God. Couldn't be better. He's going to make it with no strain. No strain at all."

Night has overtaken him. A look at the timer on his instrument panel tells him that his day lasted just 45 minutes. Darkness came suddenly. The sun, an intense white ball in the window overhead, abruptly disappeared, and the day was gone. His last sunlit glimpse of the earth had shown him the waters of the Indian Ocean, with Australia just ahead, clearly in view.

He can still see the vague land mass of Australia, although it is now indistinct and blurred. But overhead, through his window, is the most magnificent view he's ever seen: the firmament, uncensored and undiluted by the fuzzing atmosphere of the earth. The sky is an ebony black of undescribable purity, and against this backdrop myriads of multi-colored stars look unblinkingly on him like a universal Christmas tree. He remembers the summer nights when he used to lie in the backyard on the nape of his neck and stare into a star-filled sky. *This* is what he was looking for then. He knew it was there if only the cobwebs could be brushed aside. And now they have been. He wonders how much other earthbound thinking is fogged over by inability to brush aside extraneous matter, to have a look at the universe and the things that go on within it with the clarity and perspective in which he sees them now.

He wants to shout with the delight of this discovery. But another voice violates his reverie. A wonderfully familiar voice.

"Are you reading me in the capsule? We've picked you up over Australia. Put down that comic book and answer, will you?"

He smiles, and the intense thoughtfulness of the moment passes.

"Hey, buddy," he says, "you should be up here. You better hope they pull your name out of the hat for the next ride. This is something you shouldn't miss."

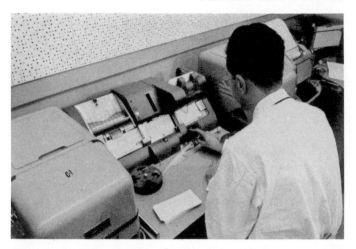

Telemetering machines at the tracking stations transmit detailed data on the physical condition of the Astronaut to Central Control where it is carefully analyzed by NASA doctors.

And then the usual questions and the same answers. He isn't tired of giving them. He doubts that he ever will be.

Dawn arrives as quickly as day had departed. As the sun bursts over the horizon, he can see the United States — almost all of it — beneath him. The Pacific is fast disappearing, and the Mississippi will soon be directly below him. In a few minutes, he will complete his first orbit of the earth. It has now been 87 minutes from launch, and he is traveling about 18,000 m.p.h. — or about 10 times the speed of a bullet shot from a rifle.

He determines to try his flight controls before darkness comes again. He's been experimenting with his hand movements, up and down, forward and back. Now he tries a more ambitious move; he reaches to open the face piece of his helmet. His hand picks up speed as it passes before his eyes, and it raps his helmet sharply. He resists an urge to shake the injured fingers. Instead he unfastens the clamp that holds his face plate, and it swings open. There is no difference in his breathing, and he knows the environmental system in the capsule is working as it should — and as his instruments indicated. Now he moves his hand in a series of tiny zigzag motions back to the hand control.

All the excitement of wringing out a new aircraft sweeps over him. Although only the retro-rockets for returning him to earth can affect the trajectory of the capsule now that it is in orbit, he *can* change its attitude — and he sets out to discover how easily and how much.

Until darkness overtakes him again near Australia, he plays with the controls, watching through his periscope and window as he changes his position relative to earth and the heavens. A twist of the control handle turns the capsule about its vertical axis; a forward-and-back motion tumbles the capsule end-over-end; and a sideways motion rolls it about the horizontal axis. He feels none of these movements; only by watching the changing vista through his periscope screen can he be sure they are actually taking place.

He reports this information to the Astronaut in Australia. An excited exchange follows, cut short only when the Australian tracking station fades from hearing, supplanted by the Hawaiian station.

He's relaxed now, and enjoying himself immensely. His second "night" passes quickly — too quickly. As he orbits the main control station at Canaveral for his third, and last circuit of the earth, he's hauled abruptly back to practicalities.

"Do you want to review the re-entry procedure while we have you on voice?" the NASA flight controller asks him.

He'd forgotten about re-entry — forgotten everything except the exhilaration of weightless flight, free of all earthly

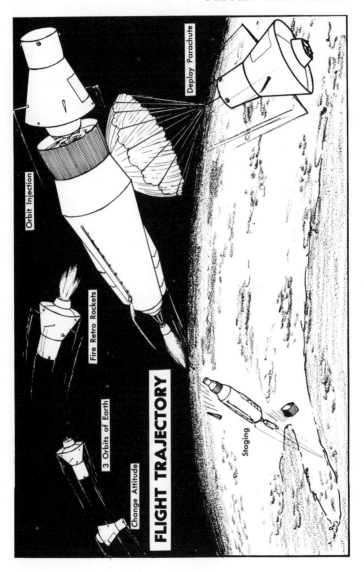

encumbrances. Soon he'll have to struggle back into earth's grasp, He feels genuine regret at the thought.

"Are you reading me in the capsule?" the range safety officer asks sharply.

He replies: "Sorry, I was day-dreaming. I don't need to review re-entry procedures. I know them cold. My timers are set. If anything goes wrong with the automatic system, I'll fire the retro-rockets. I'm fine. No problems."

There is more from the Cape. They review re-entry, any-way, and he listens patiently. Almost directly below him now lies the fleet that is waiting to rescue him from the sea the next time around. It is 5:45 in the morning in the South Atlantic. Dawn is breaking; there will be bright sun-light when he brings the capsule rocketing through the atmosphere in another 45 minutes.

In his final orbit of the earth, he simply wallows in all of the new and exciting sensations of space flight. Over Aus-tralia again, he checks his instruments with the Astronaut at the tracking station at Woomera, makes a date with him for dinner the following evening, then turns regretfully to the final — and most vital — business of the day: bringing his space ship safely through the atmosphere to a landing as close as possible to the rendezvous point in the Atlantic.

The timing devices on his instrument panel have all been set to the split second. At the precise proper instant — just north of the island of Hawaii — the clocks will automati-cally fire three solid-propellant rockets on the heat shield end of the capsule. These rockets will slow him down, and as the capsule loses speed, it will dip into the fringes of the earth's atmosphere. Here, the drag of earthly air will slow the capsule still more, pulling it farther down into the atmosphere, until finally it slows enough to permit a para-chute to open at 42,000 feet, then another at 10,000 feet to brake the final descent to a safe landing speed.

This is the most dangerous part of the trip. If the retro-rockets don't fire automatically when they should, he will have to fire them manually, thus losing at least several seconds in starting his descent — and changing his landing spot by 30 to 50 miles.

He finds some comfort in the knowledge that if the retro-rockets don't fire at all — a remote circumstance, but a possibility nevertheless — he isn't doomed to occupy a "flying coffin" orbiting the earth indefinitely. The capsule will lose enough speed on its own in a few days to dip into the atmosphere and begin an involuntary descent. When it will happen is unpredictable, but the tracking station will have him in view and will probably be able to direct rescuers to him. It isn't a pleasant prospect, however, and he resolutely turns his attention to resolving the difficulties of a normal re-entry.

There are enough problems here to keep him occupied. Chief among them is friction heat. The capsule must be angled through the atmosphere to obtain full protection from its heat shield. And, even fully shielded, it must withstand temperatures that will turn the skin of the capsule white during the peak speed of its descent.

He realizes with a start that he hasn't closed the face plate on his space suit. He completes the operation — moving his weightless arms carefully and laboriously — just as the timer flicks to zero. His hand hovers over the retro-rocket button, but the automatic system works perfectly. He watches the attitude of the capsule change through his periscope, and he feels the first indication of the intense "G" forces he'll soon be experiencing. After three hours of being delightfully weightless, he doesn't like the feeling of being pressed into his couch again.

Below him, the waters of the Pacific are a brilliant, emerald green. In a sudden surge of nostalgia, he recalls the many

As he approaches the West Coast on his third pass around the earth, the Astronaut has begun his long descent through the atmosphere to a safe landing in the Atlantic.

hours he's spent looking at the Pacific from the cockpit of a conventional plane. It seems to him, now, an old and trusted friend. In the far distance, the coastline of California — or is it Mexico? — comes into view in the first rays of dawn showering the west coast of North America.

The pressure is growing noticeably stronger. He talks briefly with the tracking station at White Sands, N. Mex., and again to the tracking officer at Eglin Air Force Base in Northern Florida. Speaking is becoming difficult for him now. His breathing is labored, and the heat intense. The stale smell of sweat drifts up through his pressure suit and into his helmet, and he doesn't like it. His stomach is already uneasy; this makes it worse.

The "G" forces on him already seem greater than at launch. He holds his attention on the instrument panel only with great effort. But the need for concentration on his controls is profound, because the capsule is beginning to oscillate badly. To the blood-draining pressure of being pushed into the couch is now added a wracking, swinging action that threatens to break him apart.

He remembers with gratitude the tumbling flights on the centrifuge when he was faced with this same problem. It takes supreme effort to make the necessary corrections now, but he makes them almost automatically, and the oscillation moderates.

Gotta keep the heat shield in front of me, he thinks. *No matter what.*

He's uncomfortably hot and queasy in the stomach. He can see nothing but sky above him, but he knows he must be over the Atlantic again, nearing the end of his re-entry arc that spanned almost half the earth's surface.

He hears someone talking but makes no effort to reply. All his energies, his resources, his will power are directed at remaining conscious. The heat has lessened, but the pressure remains intense. Is he imagining, or has it lessened too? It has. He can breathe again. The voice in his headset becomes coherent.

He must be close to the ocean. He is. Very close.

The landing is hard. It shakes him, and for an instant he wonders if somehow the capsule found a piece of land in the midst of the Atlantic. Then he feels the vehicle beneath him crest on a wave and fall suddenly off the other side, and he knows he's in the ocean. For the first time he has a sensation of claustrophobia. He wants to breathe air again. And he wants to do it right now.

Someone is repeating in his earphones: "Do you hear me in the Mercury capsule? This is the Mercury rescue fleet. If you read me, answer please."

The "please" was urgent, full of concern and on the edge of fright.

He answers: "I'm down. I'm okay. I'm going to climb out of this can — *now*. Can you see me?"

The relief and elation in the radio voice makes it almost unintelligible.

"Good news. Hang on, we'll find you. If you can manage it, come out the top of the capsule and don't sink it. Stay with it. We don't have you on radar, but we know where you went in, and we're receiving your radio signal loud and clear. We have a fix on it. Don't go away."

He manages to smile at the thought of going away as he flips off the restraining straps, surprised to find that his hands and arms are working normally again. Carefully he unzippers one glove, then the other. His headpiece comes off next. Then, reaching overhead, he loosens a piece of the instrument panel and lets it dangle forlornly in the cockpit. The steady up-on-a-crest, down-in-a-trough motion of the ocean continues, but he knows now that he isn't going to be sick, and the relief makes the motion less obnoxious to him.

With a great effort, he hoists himself from the couch and through the opening in the panel. For the first time, he's conscious of extreme physical exhaustion. But the urgent need for a look outside is greater than his exhaustion, and he breaks the seal in the hatch on top of the capsule and pokes his head into the brilliant sunshine, drawing in great draughts of ocean air.

On the horizon, clearly discernible, are several ships. A helicopter hovers overhead, and he waves to it. The pilot waves back, grinning at him. Then his eyes move beyond the helicopter, outward and upward. The sun is a flaming orange ball and the stars invisible. The sky looks crystal clear and cloudless, but he knows that over his head is an invisible curtain that hides much of the magnificence of the universe from the inhabitants of earth.

He has just raised that curtain for the first time. Now it's drawn. But it will be raised again, he knows. And each time, the raising will let in more light until maybe — just maybe — all of earth can become suffused with the light of the knowledge and wisdom to be found in limitless quantities in the universe.

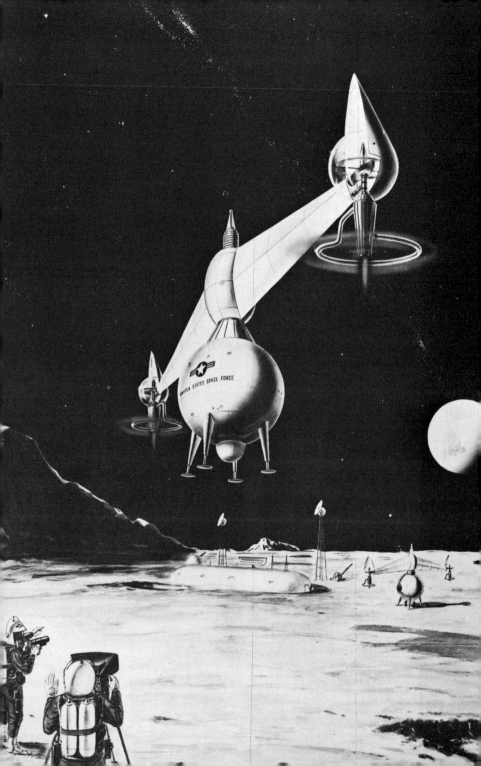

CHAPTER SEVEN

AFTER MERCURY

"In the long haul, our safety as a nation may
depend upon our achieving space superiority."
—*Lt. Gen. Bernard A. Schriever, USAF*

Where do we go from Project Mercury?

There's a tendency — when the layman considers the
Mercury program — mentally to write off space travel as a
fait accompli and turn to something else, once manned
space flight has been achieved.

The successful launching and recovery of a man from
space is, of course, but a tiny beginning. It opens a door.
Beyond that door can be found all the wonders of the universe — waiting to be discovered. Right now it seems pre-
sumptuous for man to think of exploring the far reaches of
our galaxy — and reaching out to new and undiscovered
galaxies. Yet, this is certain to happen once the first long
step into space has been taken. The solar system we now
hope to explore is tiny in relation to the known universe —
and there are many dedicated and adventurous men who

are chafing for the opportunity to reach out of this world into the new dimensions beyond.

When, how, and in what order will they reach? After successful completion of the original Mercury mission, we can expect:

Longer orbital flights around the earth, lasting from several days to several weeks;

An earth-launched manned flight to orbit the moon (1965);

A "soft" landing on the moon and return (1970);

Building of a space station from which more ambitious manned space probes can be launched (1975);

Unmanned probes of Mars and Venus, followed by manned orbiting of these two planets, then a "soft" landing on each (1980-1990).

These fantastic accomplishments can be predicted within

This is what the moon will look like to space explorers as they ease down to the moon's surface to make a first-hand examination of the earth's nearest neighbor.

the next 20 years because we *right now* have achieved most of the scientific breakthroughs necessary to bring them about. Still needed is the detailed knowledge that can only be turned up by progressive space exploration — plus larger and more powerful rockets which are now clearly possible.

Who will attain these goals first? The Russians are certainly ahead now, and whether or not they remain ahead depends almost entirely on where we peg our space program in national importance.

An unofficial but apparently authoritative article in a Russian scientific journal early in 1960 predicted that the Soviets would send a pair of men into an earth-orbit for two weeks and also launch a manned orbit of the moon by the end of the year. The same article claimed the Russians expect to send unmanned earth-shots to both Mars and Venus the following year — a distinct possibility because of the strength of the Russian rockets and the favorable position of these two planets for such a shot in 1961. Russian accomplishments don't always follow Russian claims, but the Soviet performance record in the past few years makes it necessary to consider these predictions thoughtfully. In the confusion of claims and counterclaims, one thing is very sure: the Russians are formidable opponents in space. Meeting their challenge will take the optimum of intelligence, courage, persistence, and dedication the United States can muster.

The Mercury Astronauts — who fill these requirements admirably — will be in the vanguard of our space forces, not just until the manned Mercury capsule is successfully launched, but for years afterward as well. Their contributions to our space effort will probably be redoubled once manned flight has been achieved. As pioneers in a growing field of great national importance, they will head up various phases of further space exploration — including the

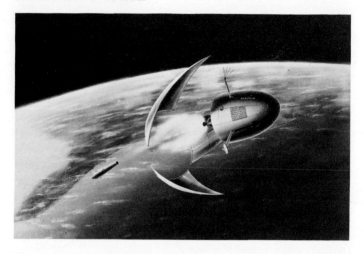

The development of higher-energy fuels will make it possible to put large unmanned satellites like this one into orbit at distances upward of 20,000 miles from the earth.

training of a much larger force of American astronauts. They are men in whom this nation can put confidence. They have been well chosen to lead the free world into space; they can lead us equally well in the contest for space superiority that will inevitably follow the first manned flights.

Where will we look once we have mastered the ability to launch and recover manned space ships? The moon will be the first target of space travelers. It is a near neighbor by interplanetary standards — about 238,000 miles from earth.

There have been two basic plans set forth for reaching it with a manned flight: by a direct shot from earth, or via a ferrying station orbiting the earth. Because it will be some years before a space station can be built, the moon will probably be reached first by men riding a vehicle launched from earth.

The six-to-nine-million-pound-thrust Nova rocket now

being developed by NASA (and due to be operational about 1968), will be capable of powering a space ship from earth to the moon in two and one-half days. The first three stages of this rocket will accelerate the ship to a speed of 25,000 m.p.h. — sufficient to propel the vehicle out of the earth's atmosphere and leave enough momentum for coasting through the vacuum of outer space to the vicinity of the moon. A fourth-stage rocket will lower the vehicle to the moon's surface. The fifth stage will blast the space traveler off the moon and back into an orbit of earth, from which the moon ship will enter the atmosphere much as the Mercury capsule. Such a vehicle would weigh more than four million pounds (mostly fuel) at launch, but less than 9,000 pounds on its return to earth.

A trip to the moon from a manned space station would be much easier and could carry a larger payload than a rocket fired from earth to moon. The problem here, of course, is that the space stations haven't been built yet and probably won't be for another decade or more. When these spatial jumping-off-places are finally established, they will orbit earth at speeds of at least 17,400 m.p.h. It will take only a brief (probably about two-minute) rocket burst to provide enough additional speed to send a vehicle from one of these orbiting space stations to the moon. And almost any shape vehicle can make the trip since streamlining has no beneficial effect in the vacuum of space.

Building the space stations, however, is a highly complex business. The structural members will have to be carried a thousand miles into space piece-by-piece in rocket ships, and dumped for later assembly. These pieces of cargo will become artificial satellites, holding to the same orbit as the ships that released them.

Construction engineers wearing pressure suits, carrying oxygen for breathing, and fastened by some sort of artificial umbilical cord to their mother ship, will then pluck the structural pieces they need from orbit and put them together like an interstellar jigsaw puzzle — while the rocket ships return to earth for additional loads. This procedure will be repeated until the station is completed. It will take many years to build, require delicate accuracy and reliability in the launching of the freight rockets — and will be staggeringly expensive. *Yet, it can unquestionably be done* — as soon as powerful enough rockets are available. In a very few years, the United States will have to decide whether it wants to foot the bill for such an operation. The alternative is to give Russia virtual carte blanche in space.

Brig. Gen. Homer Boushey, the Air Force deputy director of research and development, said recently: "I for one would not like the Russians to prove to us that the moon is a useful military site, for our future may be determined by the answer. Shall we or the Soviets find that answer?"

Using an orbiting station as a base, space explorers could venture almost anywhere. To reach other planets in our solar system, the primary restriction would no longer be one of power, but rather time and distance. Once the necessary burst of speed is attained to achieve a given destination in space, the space ship can coast incredible distances. And these speeds are now within the reach of men if the launching could be made from a space platform. For, once a space ship has escaped earth's gravity, a lesser amount of power is required to reach other planets millions of miles away.

But, unfortunately, heavier loads of fuel and supplies are needed. Even at speeds of 25,000 m.p.h., interplanetary distances are so vast that time becomes a major limiting factor. Man must be able to carry with him enough supplies to meet his needs for long periods of time — and the space ship must also perform with almost perfect reliability since there are no repair stations in space. These are the two principal

A large manned satellite is a necessary step of space exploration. Way stations to space—like the one conceived here—would be used as refueling stops on the way to other planets.

problems which will have to be solved before the space traveler can set his sights much beyond the moon.

When he does, he will fix his attention first on Venus and Mars. At their closest points to earth, Venus is 26 million miles distant and Mars about 35 million miles away. Of the two, Mars seems to hold the greater attraction — probably because of all the planets in our solar system, it appears to offer the best possibility of sustaining — or having once sustained — some sort of life similar to the life we know.

Estimates of the time required to send a manned flight from earth to Mars vary from 50 to 250 days. Keeping men alive and sane in a small sealed container in which they are weightless for this length of time presents difficult medical and logistical problems. Additional problems include:

Temperatures in space ranging from 2,000° above to 300° below zero;

Flying meteors and radiation from cosmic rays about which we still know very little;

Electromechanical equipment with such a low failure probability that, according to one scientist, "If we had sealed 100 space-ship systems in a vault eight and one-half months ago and not touched any of them in the meantime but merely supplied them with electrical power, we could open the vault today and expect to find 99 of them in perfect running condition;"

Finally, according to Dr. Earl C. Slipher, director of the Lowell Observatory where the International Mars Committee makes its headquarters, we must have "a fuel vastly more efficient than any now available."

For this reason, the most profound immediate advances in space science can be expected in the area of power systems and fuels. There are two basic demands on spatial power systems: to break loose from the earth's restraining atmosphere; and to power long-distance flights around the solar system. Although we have accomplished the first on a number of occasions, we will have to be able to put up much heavier payloads than we have so far if we hope to bring off interplanetary travel. This means we need some radical power improvements in order to meet both of the basic demands for space flight.

Many of these improvements are well beyond the dream stage, and some are solidly established on the road to actual production. Modifications in space power systems are being carried out in three principal types of powerplants.

(1) *Improved Rocket Engines.* Russia has already demonstrated that considerable additional power can be obtained from existing rocket-engine concepts. We are now at work developing chemically-fueled rockets which will far surpass the engines presently being used by the Soviets (who in turn will be improving theirs).

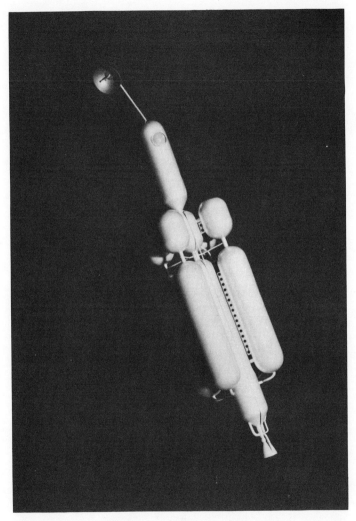

This is the sort of vehicle that may be used for flight around the moon and back in the next decade. The four fuel and oxidizer tanks around the structure would be jettisoned when empty.

The best known of the new American rockets is the Saturn — one of the highest priority projects in the American space program. Saturn is being developed by Wernher von Braun and his Huntsville (Ala.) team. Saturn involves the clustering of eight intermediate rocket engines to produce a thrust (about four times as powerful as the Atlas) that will blast 30,000 pounds into an orbit 300 miles above the earth's surface. Saturn will also be powerful enough to send several men into an orbit around the moon and return them to earth.

After Saturn (due in 1964-65) will come a single-chambered rocket engine in the same thrust class (about a million-and-a-half pounds). Known as the F-1, it was put under contract to North American's Rocketdyne Division in January, 1960. The F-1 will deliver in a single engine the equivalent of the thrust produced by Saturn's eight-

Here is a model of the Saturn, the rocket on which many of our space hopes are riding. Examining it are Dr. Von Braun, center, scientist Karl Heimbur, and Maj. Gen. John Medaris (now retired).

Each of the Saturn engines — shown here in a full-scale mock-up — will provide a thrust of 188,000 pounds. A cluster of these powerful engines will propel a heavy payload into outer space.

179

engine cluster. The next step in rocket-engine development will be a cluster of F-1's, and eventually a single-chambered five-million-pound thrust engine capable of putting a 350,-000-pound payload on the moon. The Nova, mentioned earlier, will consist of a cluster of these powerful new engines.

(2) *Thermonuclear Power* — Many scientists are looking beyond the chemical rocket engine — with its insatiable appetite for bulky fuel — to other means of space propulsion. The most promising of these alternative methods now appears to be thermonuclear power.

According to Hugh Dryden, NASA's deputy administrator, "The potentialities of the use of nuclear energy in the exploration of space are great, both for primary and auxiliary power. Nuclear energy will probably find its first space application in auxiliary power systems in the next 10 years. A practicable nuclear rocket will probably be demonstrated toward the end of this period, possibly as an upper stage of an interplanetary probe, with the reactor being started after escape velocity has been reached."

Dr. Thomas F. Dixon, chief engineer of Rocketdyne, thinks it will take about 25 years to develop a thermonuclear space engine. But he also believes that broadening interplanetary exploration will demand propulsion systems that can produce more power from smaller fuel sources — which makes the thermonuclear engine, using the fusion principle of the H-bomb, particularly attractive.

(3) *Electrical Propulsion* — NASA's Lewis Research Center in Cleveland early in 1960 came up with the prototype of an electrical space engine using ion beams powered by a turbo-generator — driven, in turn, by a nuclear reactor.

Research at Lewis indicates that low-thrust electrical propulsion systems may be the answer for the movement of space vehicles once they've escaped from the earth's atmosphere. Dr. Ernst Stuhlinger, director of research projects for Von Braun's Huntsville group, has designed an electrically-propelled space ship which revolves slowly in the direction opposite its turbine and generator, thus providing the crew with "artificial gravity." Dr. Stuhlinger estimates his reactor would require about 12 tons of uranium to provide sufficient electric power for a trip to Mars and back.

Other ideas are being investigated, including the use of solar heating devices to convert radiation gathered from the sun into thermal energy to power the space ship in the long haul between planets. The most fantastic power proposal — in an area that seems constructed of pure fantasy anyway — has been put forward by Dr. T. C. Tsu, an aerodynamicist at the Westinghouse Research Laboratories.

Dr. Tsu suggests that the cheapest, simplest, and lightest means of propelling man through space is by means of a sail. His solar sail — made of aluminum foil or lightweight plastic no more than one-ten-thousandth of an inch thick — would gather in the energy of the sun to propel the space craft. Dr. Tsu sees the sail as parachute-shaped; in size, the sail would have to be larger than the perimeter of the Pentagon to carry a payload of one thousand pounds.

While scientists and engineers are wrestling with such fundamental problems as power sources, other space buffs are struggling with a multitude of smaller problems complicating space travel. For example, under study are:

Metallic cloth suits to hold weightless passengers in their seats through magnets built into the seats;

Exercise machines to keep space passengers from coming home with broken-down muscles after long hours of confinement in a space ship;

An interstellar garden on board the space ship which would use human wastes to fertilize a crop of algae which in turn would provide water, oxygen, and food for a species of fish called the *Telapia* — supposedly highly palatable to human beings;

"Do-it-yourself" oxygen kits for space voyagers on extended trips.

Admittedly, this sort of frou-frou — which is given wide publicity (and which is also serious business to fill a serious need) — sours a great many people on giving fair consideration to the importance of our space program. It is terribly important that we not let the frills get in the way of the substance of space exploration. As Gen. Schriever pointed out, it is indeed "a deadly serious business."

Yet, because space travel has so long been a fit subject in America only for comic strips and small boys in plastic helmets, it is extremely difficult to put it across to hard-headed citizens raised in a generation of depression, war, and deficit spending. It's been made doubly difficult by the excesses of some of the experts and pseudo-experts who have garbed the whole space business in such thick layers of technical jargon that it defies understanding by lay taxpayers, many of whom aren't much interested in the first place.

This communication gap needs sorely to be bridged. The support and understanding of these apathetic or disenchanted taxpayers is needed. Reduced to its elements, a simple matter of survival for this country and this way of life is directly involved.

No matter how wildly unnecessary and improbable space travel may seem at this moment, the explorations just described *are going to happen within the next few decades.* Our future as a nation will depend to a very large extent on what we, versus the Russians, accomplish in space during that period. And where we stand will depend — to a comparably large extent — on how well the importance of the space contest is presented to and supported by the American people.

At the moment, we're decidedly short on both support and understanding. This has affected the speed, energy, and efficiency with which our space explorations have been conducted. Before we can move in any direction, we need to assess our man-into-space program as it stands today.

I have had the rare privilege, as a reporter, of taking a leisurely look at the Indians—not the chiefs—of the United States' man-into-space program. As far as I know, I'm the only reporter to have done so — with the exception of the representatives of LIFE magazine, whose point of view is necessarily restricted by their investment in the personal story of the Astronauts. I talked with the Astronauts individually and in a group. I interviewed a number of the scientists and technicians who have been working with Project Mercury from the beginning of the program. From these conversations, from a first-hand look at what is going on at NASA's Langley Field headquarters and from reading hundreds of thousands of words spoken or written about the Mercury program, several things — none of which have been impressed on the American public — seem very clear to me:

(1) There is very little sense of urgency in the Mercury program. By no stretch of the imagination could it be considered a crash program. There are many indications that quite the contrary is true, even though a DX priority (the highest national priority) has been assigned to Project Mercury.

For example, as far as I could see, there is no overtime being put in by anyone connected with Project Mercury at Langley Field. The atmosphere is much like a routine business office — with business as usual. To one who has smelled and tasted the urgency of war, the contrast is marked. Project Mercury is truly being conducted as the civilian peacetime scientific program that the President describes it as

— well-insulated both from military rivalry and any directed aura of excessive need, haste, or urgency.

This is reflected in the Astronauts' ridiculous travel arrangements by commercial transportation — already discussed earlier. This impressed me so much because it epitomizes the two major philosophies at the top of our government regarding the Mercury program. First, the lack of sufficient funds to provide maintenance for an aircraft for the Austronauts' exclusive use illustrates the emphasis on budget, on holding costs down. Second, the casual regard for time illustrates the lack of urgency felt at the top for getting a man into space before the Russians do.

(2) There is *not* unanimity of opinion among the major participants in the Mercury program that it is being handled in the way it should. There is considerable frustration and restiveness at the operational level of Project Mercury.

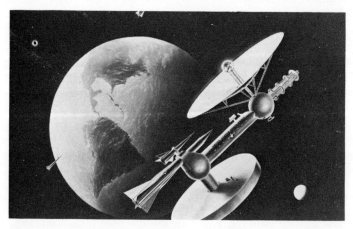

This type of space station, powered by solar batteries and designed to orbit up to 5,000 miles above earth, would be used for navigation, communication, and astronautical observation.

We have here the curious contradiction of the people whose lives are most directly affected wanting to get on with the program at all costs — because many of them are burning with a sense of urgency that is almost daily being dampened by public proclamations from the top.

Most of the NASA and Project Mercury officials who disagree with our leisurely wandering into space — as contrasted with an all-out program aimed at a clearly defined and urgent set of goals *including licking the Russians* — have been forced to remain quiet and do their jobs as best they can within the limitations imposed on them.

Even the Astronauts are not entirely in accord on this point. Some of them feel that the program is progressing in the well-ordered manner that it should. But others are building up a head of steam that threatens to blow off more and more frequently — as when one of them told me: "I'll tell you one thing for damn sure. We'll get that first Redstone flight in the air before the end of 1960 if I have to light the match myself."

(3) We are being cautious to the point of diminishing returns in the technical portion of the Mercury program.

An Astronaut told me plaintively: "I have yet to test an airplane that was pronounced 100-percent reliable and safe beforehand. Yet, sometimes it seems that's what they're trying to achieve with this Mercury hardware. Hell, if we keep trying for that, we'll never get this bird off the ground. There's got to be *some* element of risk involved. We know that, and we're willing to take it. We've been taking risks for years."

This is a trained, thoughtful engineer-pilot speaking — not a vainglorious child sounding off for an appreciative audience.

It's difficult to argue against safety. The motives of those who insist on absolute reliability and safety in the Mercury

This unmanned space vehicle—to be launched from an earth satellite—has been designed to examine the surface of Mars from an distance of 8,000 to 9,000 miles.

program are, of course, simply to protect the life and limb of the Astronauts. Yet some of the pilots themselves look upon the flight as a calculated risk, and they feel that growing security-consciousness in America is prevailing against calculated risks — to the detriment of our virility, vitality, and progress.

None of these men want to die — gloriously or otherwise. But they do want to bring off successful, manned space flight, and they want to do it before anyone else does. They are willing to accept some risk of the former in order to achieve the latter. It's as simple as that.

There's another potent reason for the insistence that every minute precaution be taken for the protection of the Mercury pilot — even if it delays the program out of all proportion to the importance of the safeguard. A large portion of the American public still looks on Mercury as a frivolous stunt. If it is brought off successfully and the United States gains great prestige in the world as a result, many of these skeptics will be won over. But if the flight is attempted and fails — the result in unfavorable public opinion may well be catastrophic.

Scientists connected with the Mercury program are acutely aware of this. One of them told me, with great feeling:

"What if we kill the first man? That's what worries me. It's a life we can't spare, certainly, but it's much more than that. It might ruin the whole project — make us all look like a bunch of half-baked dreamers. We all know this thing is right and that it will work, but there's always the chance of failure the first time around, and that haunts us. It's the worst thing that could happen to the program. An initial failure could well torpedo the whole project as far as public opinion is concerned. Yet, it's a calculated risk that goes along with every pioneering exploration that's ever taken place. All our energies are directed toward preventing this

SEVEN INTO SPACE

— yet it *could* happen."

It's disheartening to realize that the American man-into-space program is so close to the quicksand of public antagonism that one technical failure could suffocate it. Yet this assessment is probably accurate, and it is certainly influencing — consciously or otherwise — the insistence on reliability in performance of the Mercury hardware over and beyond what even some of the Astronauts consider reasonable.

Of all these elements which are holding back our space program, the most important is the lack of a strong rapport at the very top with the aims and necessities of space exploration.

Putting a man into space should be a matter of considerable urgency to the United States. In the Mercury program are a number of talented people who feel they have the capabilities to be first — and are exceedingly uneasy about the circumstances now forcing them not only to swallow the second-best pill, but to use something less than all their energies in throwing it up to compete at full throttle for world leadership.

At a news conference early in 1960, President Eisenhower was asked if he thought our international prestige was at stake in the space race. He replied: "Not particularly, no."

A month later, when asked if he didn't feel any sense of urgency in catching up with the Russians, he answered that he was "always a little bit amazed at this business of catching up." He went on to say that defense was one thing and space exploration another. "Let us remember," he concluded, "this one thing; the reason for going into space . . . is purely scientific."

Several weeks later, after being badgered on the American "missile gap," the President said with some exasperation: "Now I think our people ought to have greater faith in their own system, go ahead on their own — because, let's remember, you people are the bosses of the American government . . . You can make the decisions. All you have to do is inform yourselves and you will make good decisions."

The information in this book has been offered in the hope that an informed American public will insist that we establish specific goals in space, label their pursuit "urgent," then use the magnificent intellectual and physical resources at our disposal in the United States *to the utmost of their capabilities* in pursuing these goals.

Many dedicated and thoughtful Americans are urging that we reassess and rededicate our entire space program.

Testifying before a Congressional committee in February, 1960, Maj. Gen. John Medaris, former chief of the Army Ballistic Missile Agency, said: "From a purely technical viewpoint, there is so little difference between civilian and military space programs that there is no justification for their division and resulting duplications." Medaris urged that Congress create a single, unified missile command. "Every single engineering and production facility that is involved in any kind of important space project is now involved in one or more missile projects," he added. "Since no one in authority is totally and immediately responsible for the complete mission, what is everybody's business ends up being nobody's business."

Walter Lippmann in his syndicated column a few weeks earlier said: "Men of genius cannot do what they are capable of doing if, as is the case today, they are herded into separate compartments and told to devote themselves to limited aims. They will respond best if they can believe that they are part of a great inquiry and experimentation into the nature of the universe. There is no such favoring climate today. . . . We have a materialism which regards the exploration of space and indeed the exploration of the unknown as less important than the multiplication of consumer goods."

And about the same time, the NASA's administrator, T. Keith Glennan, was telling the National Press Club: "The Russians have exploited to the fullest the psychological, the political, and the propaganda possibilities . . . of their Sputniks and their Luniks.

"In the United States, our reactions have been violent, frequent, but of very short duration. In between the Russian Sputnik and Lunik firings, we have been preoccupied with the progress of the World Series, with the standings in the pro football league, or the shabby disclosures of the TV quiz show investigations.

"Each time the Russians have launched a new space explorer, we have reacted with a tremendous clamor to do something, right now, to catch up. And almost as promptly, once we had made our outcry, we turned to personal matters of greater interest to each one of us as individuals.

"We plainly must awake to the fact that the Russians would very much prefer to gain mastery of the world without having to fire a single ICBM; that they hope to become so superior in their scientific, technological, and economic capabilities that they will win world domination through industrial power rather than through shooting wars."

These are prophetic words. But how many Americans are listening?

While the debate continues — with the participants hoping that a few Americans will look up from their sports cars and television sets and credit cards to listen — seven finely-trained young men sit on the edge of space at Langley Field, Va.

One of them was moved to tell me: "Sure we could speed up this program. People can work overtime. We could be put on a crash basis . . . But what can you expect at *our* level in view of the attitude at the very top — that we're progressing just dandy."

When I asked one of the officials of the Mercury program how much it might be speeded up if it were put on a crash basis, he told me flatly: "From three to six months."

When I put the same question to Administrator Glennan early in 1960, he refused to answer it "out of context with the rest of the program."

Glennan, of course, was on the spot. He couldn't publicly disagree with his boss, President Eisenhower — a constraint, incidentally, that not all of his subordinates felt bound by.

Glennan was caught in a bureaucratic vise. Beneath him, many of the scientists in the Mercury program — and most of the Astronauts, too — wanted to put the program into high gear, to go all-out with a strong sense of American purpose and competition to meet the Soviets head-on in space and lick the pants off them. But above him, the President of the United States benignly said we were not in a space race with the Russians.

This left Glennan — or any other NASA administrator who might succeed him — the choice of hewing to official policy publicly, or quitting. It should also have given him the freedom privately to advise his boss that thoughtful, knowledgeable participants in the program felt that some changes were urgently needed. If such advice was offered, there has been no indication that the President heeded it. Instead, we continued, apathetically, to drag our feet in putting a man into space.

In a program that is administered and staffed to a large extent by military men with a strong antipathy to insubordination, and scientists to whom political considerations are usually secondary, it is hardly surprising that few voices have been raised in dissent. But there's no doubt that the dissent exists; the truly surprising thing is that it has been articulated as much as it has.

Thus, in the end, the choice of our route into space comes back — as the President so earnestly pointed out — to the American people. According to Mr. Eisenhower, the most effective way to change our present course is for the people to insist — and *persist* — that we go all-out to compete with the Russians in space.

And the plain fact is that most Americans just don't give a damn.

We'd better start giving a damn — and soon.

Much of the battle between Communism and the free world for the minds and hopes of uncommitted men in the years ahead is going to be fought in outer space — not in armed missiles — *but in scientific accomplishment.*

Today, the vanguard of our freedom forces consists of seven young Americans waiting to be shot into space.

They deserve our understanding and support.

They ask only one thing more — the opportunity to compete at full strength and effectiveness.

They deserve that, too. Given it, they'll win.

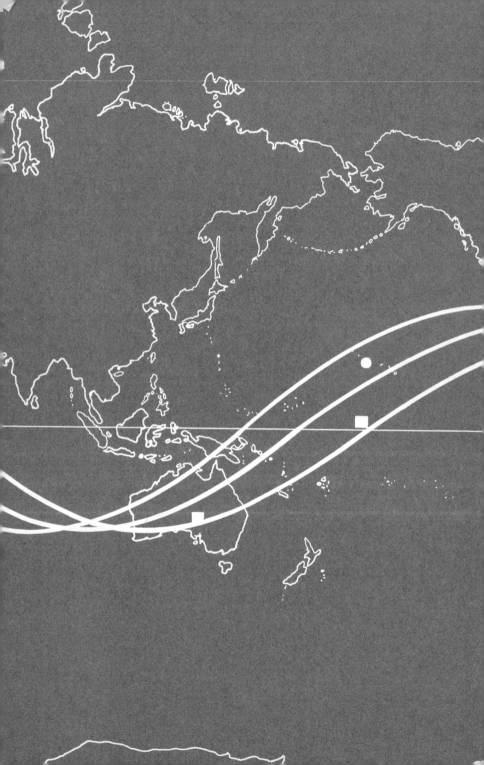